STARGAZING 2005

MONTH-BY-MONTH GUIDE TO THE NORTHERN NIGHT SKY

HEATHER COUPER & NIGEL HENBEST

HEATHER COUPER and NIGEL HENBEST are internationally recognized writers and broadcasters on astronomy, space and science. They have written more than 30 books and over 1000 articles and are the founders of an independent TV production company, specializing in factual and scientific programming.

Heather is a past President of both the British Astronomical Association and the Society for Popular Astronomy. She is a Fellow of the Royal Astronomical Society, a Fellow of the Institute of Physics and a Millennium Commissioner. Nigel has been Astronomy Consultant to New Scientist magazine, Editor of the Journal of the British Astronomical Association, and Media Consultant to the Royal Greenwich Observatory.

Published in Great Britain in 2004
by Philip's, a division of Octopus Publishing Group Ltd,
2–4 Heron Quays, London E14 4JP

Text: Heather Couper & Nigel Henbest (pp. 6–53)
Robin Scagell (pp. 61–64)
Philip's (pp. 1–5, 54–60)

ISBN-13 978-0-540-08703-7
ISBN-10 0-540-08703-3

Printed in China

Details of other Philip's titles and services can be found on our website at: **www.philips-maps.co.uk**

Title page: The Pleiades (Michael Stecker/Galaxy)

CONTENTS

The sight of diamond-bright stars sparkling against a sky of black velvet is one of the most glorious experiences that life can offer. No wonder stargazing is so popular. Learning your way around the night sky requires nothing more than patience, a reasonably clear sky and the twelve star charts included in this book.

Stargazing 2005 is a guide to the sky for every month of the year. Complete beginners will find it an essential night-time companion, while seasoned amateur astronomers will find the updates invaluable.

THE MONTHLY CHARTS

Each pair of monthly charts shows the views of the heavens looking north and south. They're useable throughout most of Europe – between 40 and 60 degrees north. Only the brightest stars are shown (otherwise we would have had to put 3000 stars on each chart, instead of about 200). This means that we plot stars down to 3rd magnitude, with a few 4th-magnitude stars to complete distinctive patterns.

USING THE STAR CHARTS

To use the charts, begin by locating the north pole star – Polaris – by using the stars of the Plough, as we describe in 'March's constellation'. When you are looking at Polaris you are facing north, with west on your left and east on your right. (West and east are reversed on star charts because they show the view look-ing up into the sky instead of down towards the ground.) The left-hand chart then shows the view you have to the north. Most of the stars you see will be circumpolar, which means that they're visible all year. The other stars rise in the east and set in the west.

Now turn and face the opposite direction, south. This is the view that changes most during the course of the year. Leo, with its prominent 'Sickle' formation, is high in the spring skies. Summer is dominated by the bright trio of Vega, Deneb and Altair. Autumn's familiar marker is the Square of Pegasus, while the winter sky is ruled over by the stars of Orion.

The charts show the sky as it appears in the late evening for each month; the exact times are noted in the caption with the chart. If you are observing in the early morning you will find that the view is different. As a rule of thumb, if you are observing two hours later than the time suggested in the caption, then the previous month's map will more accurately represent the stars on view. So, if you wish to observe at midnight in the middle of February, two hours later than the time suggested in the caption for February's chart, then the stars will appear as they are on January's chart. When using a chart for the 'wrong' month, how-ever, bear in mind that the planets and Moon will not be shown in their correct positions.

THE MOON, PLANETS AND SPECIAL EVENTS

In addition to the stars visible each month, the charts show the positions of any planets on view in the late evening. Other planets may also be visible that month, but they won't be on the chart if they have already set, or if they do not rise until early morning. Their positions are described in the text, so that you can find them if you are observing at other times.

We've also plotted the path of the Moon. Its position at full Moon is marked, together with positions at three-day intervals either side of full Moon. The dates when it reaches first quarter, full Moon, last quarter and new Moon are given in the text. Times of sunrise and sunset are also given; these are correct for London but may differ by several minutes if you live elsewhere. If there is a meteor shower in the month we mark the position from which the meteors appear to emanate – the *radiant*. More information on observing the planets and other Solar System objects is given on pages 54–57.

Once you have identified the constellations and found the planets, you'll want to know more about what's on view. Each month, we explain one object, such as a particularly interesting star or galaxy, in detail. We have also chosen a spectacular image for each month and described how it was captured. All these pictures were taken by amateur astronomers. We list details and dates of special events, such as meteor showers or eclipses, and give observing tips. Finally, each month we pick a topic related to what's on view, ranging from red giant stars to extrasolar planets, and discuss it in more detail. Where possible, all relevant objects are highlighted on the maps.

FURTHER INFORMATION

The year's star charts form the heart of the book, providing material for many enjoyable observing sessions. For background information turn to pages 54–57, where diagrams help to explain, among other things, the movement of the planets and why we see eclipses.

Although there's plenty to see with the naked eye, many observers use binoculars or telescopes, and some choose to record their observations using cameras, CCDs or webcams. For a round-up of what's new in observing technology, go to pages 61–64, where equipment expert Robin Scagell shares his knowledge.

If you have already invested in binoculars or a telescope then you can explore the deep sky – nebulae (starbirth sites), star clusters and galaxies. On pages 58–60 we list recommended deep sky objects, constellation by constellation. Use the appropriate month's maps to see which constellations are on view, and then choose your targets. The table of 'limiting magnitude' (page 58) will help you to decide if a particular object is visible with your equipment.

Happy stargazing!

This is the most exciting month of the year for appreciating the magnificence of the starry sky. Darkness falls early, and the nights are often frosty and clear. Centre-stage of the heavens is the glorious constellation of **Orion**, fighting his adversary, Taurus the Bull – accompanied by his trusty hounds, **Canis Major** and **Canis Minor**. Just above the main body of Taurus is the tiny star cluster of the **Pleiades**, looking for all the world like 'fireflies tangled in a silver braid', in the words of the poet Tennyson.

January is also the time to see some of the brightest stars in the sky, including *the* brightest – **Sirius**, in the constellation of Canis Major. But this year the focus of the month isn't a star, but a planet. Just below the stars of Gemini is the bright planet **Saturn**, which hit the headlines last July, with the arrival of the US Cassini spaceprobe. This month, Europe's Huygens craft – now detached from Cassini – will land on Saturn's biggest moon, Titan. It is a daring mission, and all the world will be watching.

JANUARY'S CONSTELLATION

Orion is one of the most recognizable constellations in the sky, and one of the rare star-groupings that looks like its namesake – a giant of a man with a sword below his belt, wielding a club above his head. Orion is fabled in mythology as the ultimate hunter. The constellation is dominated by two brilliant stars: at top left is blood-red **Betelgeuse** (known to sci-fi fans as 'Beetlejuice'), and at bottom right is the even more brilliant blue-white **Rigel**.

The two stars could hardly be more different. Betelgeuse is a cool, bloated, dying star – known as a red giant – over 300 times the size of the Sun. Rigel is a vigorous young star more than twice as hot as our Sun (its surface temperature is 12,000°C) and over 50,000 times as bright. The famous 'belt of Orion' is made up of the stars Alnitak (left), Alnilam and Mintaka (right), below which hangs Orion's sword. The Orion Nebula is our 'Object of the month'.

▼The sky at 10 pm in the middle of January, with Moon-positions marked at intervals of three days and at full Moon. The positions of the stars are also correct for

WEST
PISCES
Square of Pegasus
TRIANGULUM
Algol
PEGASUS
ANDROMEDA
PERSEUS
Capella
Deneb
CEPHEUS
CASSIOPEIA
Zenith
AURIGA
CYGNUS
Polaris
Radiant of Quadrantids
DRACO
URSA MINOR
The Sickle
HERCULES
The Plough
URSA MAJOR
LEO
CANES VENATICI
BOÖTES
VIRGO
NORTH
NE
EAST

11 pm at the beginning of January, and 9 pm at the end of the month. The planets move slightly relative to the stars during the month.

WEST

PISCES · 16 Jan · Mira · CETUS · TRIANGULUM · ARIES · 19 Jan · TAURUS · ERIDANUS · Algol · PERSEUS · Pleiades · Aldebaran · Rigel · LEPUS · Capella · Zenith · AURIGA · 22 Jan · GEMINI · Betelgeuse · ORION · Orion Nebula · CANIS MAJOR · COLUMBA · SOUTH · Castor · Pollux · Saturn · CANIS MINOR · Procyon · Sirius · Adhara · URSA MAJOR · The Sickle · 25 Jan · CANCER · HYDRA · PUPPIS · LEO · Regulus · 28 Jan · VIRGO

EAST

PLANETS ON VIEW

Saturn, in the constellation of Gemini, is the planet in the news this month, and on 13 January it draws closest to the Earth in its orbit. Everything's relative, however, with the two worlds still 1200 million km (750 million miles) apart. The event is known as an opposition, which is defined as when the Sun, the Earth and a planet are in line (see page 55). Saturn shines at magnitude −0.4, more brilliantly than any of the stars on view apart from **Sirius**. The next day, 14 January, Europe's Huygens probe plunges into the atmosphere of Saturn's moon Titan, destined for a soft landing, we hope.

Jupiter, Saturn's larger cousin, rises at around midnight in the constellation of Virgo. It's brighter than any of the stars, at magnitude −2.1. Reasonable binoculars will show the four largest moons – Io, Europa, Ganymede and Callisto – but these are just the biggest in a family of some 60 moons. Mid-month, the giant planet passes close to the 4th-magnitude star Theta Virginis: it will look as if Jupiter has yet another moon!

Mars rises at around 5 am all month. Shining at magnitude +1.5, it moves from the constellation Scorpius to Ophiuchus.

Venus, brilliant at magnitude −3.9, follows Mars, rising at 7 am at the beginning of January and 7.30 am at the end.

Mercury (magnitude −0.3) lies above Venus in the morning twilight early in the month; it will drop out of sight by mid-January.

Uranus (magnitude +5.9) lies in Aquarius and sets at around 8 pm.

Neptune is too close to the Sun to be visible this month.

January's Object Orion Nebula
January's Picture
Radiant of Quadrantids

Saturn
Moon

MOON		
Date	Time	Phase
3	5.50 pm	Last Quarter
10	12.04 pm	New Moon
17	06.59 am	First Quarter
25	10.36 am	Full Moon

MOON

On 10 January, the Moon is at its closest point to the Earth for the year – 'just' 356,600 km (221,600 miles) away. Theoretically, the Moon is then its largest apparent size in the sky, but it's also the time of new Moon, so we won't actually see it! Expect impressive shows of the crescent Moon, though, just before and after new Moon.

The last quarter Moon passes close to Jupiter on 3/4 January, and again on 31 January. As a very narrow crescent, the Moon is near Mars on the morning of 7 January, and it passes to the right of Venus and Mercury on 8 January. The Moon passes just below the **Pleiades** star cluster on 19/20 January. The almost-full Moon lies near Saturn on 23 January.

SPECIAL EVENTS

2 January: Earth is at perihelion – the point in its orbit where it is closest to the Sun. The Earth travels around the Sun in an elliptical path, and on this date it lies 147 million km (91 million miles) from our local star.

3 January: It's the maximum of the **Quadrantid** meteor shower. These shooting stars are tiny particles of dust shed by Comet Machholz, which burn up as they enter the Earth's atmosphere. Perspective makes them appear to emanate from one spot in the sky, the *radiant* (marked on the star chart). The peak of the shower – when you may see up to 100 meteors an hour – is very narrow and unpredictable. This year, moonlight in Europe will all but drown out the meteors, but those living in North America stand a better chance.

◉ **Viewing tip**

It may sound obvious, but if you want to stargaze at this most glorious time of year, dress up warmly! Lots of layers are better than a heavy coat because they trap air next to your skin. Heavy-soled boots stop the frost creeping up your legs, and a woolly hat really does stop one-third of your body heat escaping through the top of your head. And – alas – no hipflask of whisky: alcohol constricts the veins, making you feel even colder.

◄ This beautiful image of the Pleiades (or Seven Sisters) star cluster (M45) was captured by Michael Stecker, with a 155 mm refractor on ISO 400 film. Two separate exposures were scanned and added with a computer.

JANUARY'S OBJECT

Look at Orion's 'sword' and – on a clear night – you'll detect the **Orion Nebula** as a small fuzzy patch among the line of stars. Through binoculars, or a small telescope, the patch looks like a small cloud in space. It *is* a cloud, but at 15 light years across, it's hardly small. Only the distance of the Orion Nebula – 1500 light years – diminishes it. Yet it is one of the nearest regions of star formation to the Earth, containing at least 150 fledgling stars (known as protostars), which have condensed out of the gas.

This 'star factory' is lit by fierce radiation from a small cluster of newly born stars called 'the Trapezium', which are beautiful to look at through a small telescope. The Orion Nebula is part of a huge gas complex in the Orion region; it may have enough material to make 500,000 stars in the future.

JANUARY'S PICTURE

The beautiful nebulosity in the picture reveals that the **Pleiades** have blundered into a cloud of gas and dust in space. The stars are so hot that the gas and dust reflect their searingly blue colour. Unfortunately, the nebulosity is only visible on photographic or webcam images and not usually through a telescope.

JANUARY'S TOPIC
Titan

On 14 January, Europe's Huygens probe will plunge into the dense atmosphere of the ringed planet's largest moon, Titan.

Titan is an enigma. At 5150 km (3200 miles) across, it is larger than the planets Mercury and Pluto. Discovered by the Dutch astronomer Christiaan Huygens in the seventeenth century, Titan has been unwilling to give up its secrets. Unlike any other moon in the Solar System, it has a very thick atmosphere. It is made of nitrogen – like the atmosphere of Earth – but its pressure is 50% greater than ours. When the US spaceprobe Voyager 1 flew by Saturn hoping for a close-up view of Titan's surface, all that was visible were thick orange clouds.

Huygens is on an audacious mission. It will parachute through Titan's clouds and land on what could be a solid surface, or what may be an ocean of natural gas, such as liquid methane and ethane. Huygens may even have to contend with erupting volcanoes. But cameras and instruments on board the craft will get the measure of the moon. Titan's temperature is −180°C, and some astronomers have referred to Titan as 'an Earth in deep freeze'. Its chemistry is so similar to that of the early Earth that researchers hope the Huygens probe will uncover some clues as to how life started on our own planet – and if it is ever likely to arise on Titan in the future.

SUNRISE AND SUNSET

Date	Rise (am)	Set (pm)
1	8.06	4.03
2	8.06	4.04
3	8.06	4.05
4	8.06	4.06
5	8.05	4.07
6	8.05	4.08
7	8.05	4.10
8	8.04	4.11
9	8.04	4.12
10	8.03	4.14
11	8.03	4.15
12	8.02	4.17
13	8.01	4.18
14	8.00	4.20
15	8.00	4.21
16	7.59	4.23
17	7.58	4.24
18	7.57	4.26
19	7.56	4.28
20	7.55	4.29
21	7.54	4.31
22	7.52	4.33
23	7.51	4.34
24	7.50	4.36
25	7.49	4.38
26	7.48	4.40
27	7.46	4.41
28	7.45	4.43
29	7.43	4.45
30	7.42	4.47
31	7.40	4.49

This month, **Saturn** continues to dominate the heavens, riding high in the sky in the constellation of **Gemini**. But there are signs that spring is on the way. The brilliant winter stars are starting to drift towards the west as Earth travels around the Sun on its annual journey, so that we see a slowly shifting view of our cosmic environs.

Capella, the brightest star in the constellation of **Auriga** (the Charioteer), has moved from the overhead position it claimed for much of winter, and **Orion** has started to shuffle towards the wings. But February is an excellent time to see **Canis Major**, dominated by **Sirius**, the brightest star in the sky. Alas, from northern latitudes, Sirius is very low in the sky, although this can make for some sensational visual effects: you'll often see the star twinkling and flashing all the colours of the rainbow. This has nothing to do with Sirius, but a lot to do with the Earth's atmosphere. Looking at the stars through the atmosphere is like looking at your surroundings from the bottom of a swimming pool. As the water shifts and ripples, you get a distorted view. It's the same with Earth's atmosphere: it's always on the move, so it makes the stars appear to twinkle. It also refracts starlight, creating the multicolour light show.

FEBRUARY'S CONSTELLATION

You can't ignore **Gemini** in February. It's high in the south, and – even if you live in a light-polluted city – **Saturn** is an excellent locator for the Heavenly Twins. The constellation is dominated by the stars **Castor** and **Pollux**. They are of similar brightness and represent the heads of a pair of twins, with their stellar bodies running in parallel lines of stars towards the west.

Legend has it that Castor and Pollux were twins, conceived on the same night by the princess Leda. On the night she married the King of Sparta, wicked old Zeus (Jupiter) invaded the marital suite, disguised as a swan. Pollux was the

▼ The sky at 10 pm in mid-February, with Moon-positions marked at intervals of three day and at full Moon. The positions of the stars are also correct for

11 pm at the beginning of February, and 9 pm at the end of the month. The planets move slightly relative to the stars during the month.

result of the liaison with Zeus – and therefore immortal – while Castor was merely a human being. The pair were so devoted to each other that Zeus decided to grant Castor honorary immortality, and he placed both Castor and Pollux among the stars.

Castor is an amazing star. It's not just one star, but a family of six. Even through a small telescope, you can see that Castor is a double star, comprising two stars circling each other. Both of these stars are double (although you need special equipment to detect this), and then there's another outlying star, visible through a telescope, which also turns out to be double.

PLANETS ON VIEW

Saturn, in Gemini, is still the planet of the month, visible high in the south at magnitude –0.2. Good binoculars – used from a dark site – will reveal its largest moon, Titan, recipient of the Huygens probe last month.

Jupiter is starting to make an appearance on our chart, rising at around 10 pm in the constellation of Virgo. At magnitude –2.3, it's seven times brighter than Saturn. On the night of 19/20 February, it passes even closer to the star Theta Virginis than it did last month.

Mars is still a morning object, rising at 5 am in early February and at 4.30 am later in the month. Still comparatively faint, at magnitude +1.3, Mars is moving quickly through the stars of Sagittarius.

Mercury, **Venus**, **Uranus** and **Neptune** are all too close to the Sun to be seen in February.

WEST

PISCES
CETUS
PERSEUS
TAURUS
15 Feb
Pleiades
Aldebaran
Crab Nebula
ERIDANUS
LEPUS
Rigel
ORION
Betelgeuse
Capella
AURIGA
18 Feb
GEMINI
Castor
Pollux
Saturn
CANCER
Procyon
CANIS MINOR
Sirius
CANIS MAJOR
Adhara
Zenith
21 Feb
The Sickle
Regulus
HYDRA
PUPPIS
URSA MAJOR
LEO
24 Feb
VIRGO
27 Feb
Jupiter

SOUTH

SW

SE

EAST

February's Object
Crab Nebula

February's Picture

Jupiter
Saturn
Moon

MOON		
Date	Time	Phase
2	7.31 am	Last Quarter
8	10.29 pm	New Moon
16	0.18 am	First Quarter
24	04.58 am	Full Moon

MOON

The waning crescent Moon lies near Mars on the morning of 5 February. It passes Saturn on the nights of 19 and 20 February, a few days before full Moon. On 26 and 27 February, the gibbous Moon moves past Jupiter in the constellation of Virgo.

FEBRUARY'S OBJECT

This month, we focus on Taurus the Bull, homing in on a small region above his 'lower horn'. There, in 1054, Chinese astronomers witnessed the appearance of a 'new star', which outshone all the other stars in the sky. Visible in daylight for 23 days, it remained in the night sky for nearly two years. But this was no new star: it was a *supernova*, that is, an old star on the way out, exploding because it was overweight.

Today, we see the remnants of the star as the **Crab Nebula**, so named by the nineteenth-century Irish astronomer Lord Rosse because it resembled a crab's pincers. Even today, the debris is still expanding from the wreckage, and it now measures 15 light years across.

At the centre of the Crab Nebula is the core of the dead star, which has collapsed to become a pulsar. This tiny, but superdense object – only the size of a city, but with the mass of the

⦿ *Viewing tip*

When you first go out to observe, you may be disappointed at how few stars you can see in the sky. But wait for around twenty minutes, and you'll be amazed at how your night vision improves. The reason is that the pupil of your eye gets larger to make the best of the darkness. Observers call this 'dark adaption', and it also involves the increased production in the retina of a chemical called rhodopsin, which dramatically increases the eye's sensitivity.

SUNRISE AND SUNSET		
Date	Rise (am)	Set (pm)
1	7.39	4.50
2	7.37	4.52
3	7.36	4.54
4	7.34	4.56
5	7.32	4.58
6	7.31	4.59
7	7.29	5.01
8	7.27	5.03
9	7.26	5.05
10	7.24	5.07
11	7.22	5.09
12	7.20	5.10
13	7.18	5.12
14	7.16	5.14
15	7.14	5.16
16	7.13	5.18
17	7.11	5.20
18	7.09	5.21
19	7.07	5.23
20	7.05	5.25
21	7.03	5.27
22	7.01	5.29
23	6.58	5.30
24	6.56	5.32
25	6.54	5.34
26	6.52	5.36
27	6.50	5.38
28	6.48	5.39

◄ The Moon at first quarter, as photographed by astronomer Robin Scagell from Buckinghamshire, UK, using a 210 mm reflecting telescope on ISO 64 film.

Sun – is spinning around furiously at 30 times a second and emitting beams of radiation like a lighthouse. You can just make out the Crab Nebula through a small telescope, but it is faint.

FEBRUARY'S PICTURE

The huge dark areas that make up part of the 'face' of the 'man in the Moon' are actually craters excavated by a bombardment of giant asteroids some 3.8 billion years ago. The impacts were so deep that basalt welled up from the Moon's interior to make the smooth plains we see today.

FEBRUARY'S TOPIC
Star names

Why do the brightest stars have such strange names? The reason is that they date from antiquity, and have been passed down the generations ever since. The original western star names – like the original constellations – were probably Babylonian or Chaldean, but few of these survive. The Greeks took up the baton after that, and the name of the star Sirius is a direct result. It derives from *seirios*, meaning 'scorching', which is appropriate for such a brilliant star.

The Romans were not particularly interested in astronomy, but nevertheless left their mark on the sky. In the constellation of Gemini, Pollux is a latinization of Polydeuces – the twin's original name in Greek. Capella also has Roman roots: the bright star now moving from its position overhead in winter is a diminutive version of *capra* (goat). It literally means 'the little she-goat', which is a bit of an understatement for a star over 100 times brighter than the Sun!

The Arabs were largely responsible for the star names we have inherited today. Working in the so-called 'Dark Ages' between the 6th and 10th centuries AD, they took over the naming of the sky – hence the number of stars beginning with the letters 'al' (Arabic for 'the'). Aldebaran, the brightest star in Taurus, comes from *Al Dabaran*, meaning 'the follower' because he was perceived as chasing the Pleiades (Seven Sisters) across the sky. Rigel, in Orion, also has Arabic roots: it means left leg.

The most remembered star name in the sky is Orion's Betelgeuse. For some time, it was gloriously interpreted as 'the armpit of the central one' or even 'the armpit of the sacred one'. But scholars have pointed out that the 'B' in Betelgeuse turned out to be a mistranslation. So, as a result of the mists of time, we're none the wiser as to how our distant ancestors really identified this fiery red star.

Spring is officially here. On 20 March, the Sun reaches the Vernal (or Spring) Equinox, which marks the cross-over between winter and summer. The Earth is tilted at 23.5 degrees with respect to its orbital path, which means that the north pole points away from the Sun between September and March – hence our northern winter – and towards it between March and September, when we enjoy summer.

On 20 March, the Sun hovers above the equator, marking the end of winter and the beginning of spring. This change is reflected in the sky, with the arrival of the spring con-stellations **Leo** and **Virgo**. On 27 March, British Summer time begins, when the clocks go for-ward by one hour.

MARCH'S CONSTELLATION

Ursa Major – whose brightest stars are usually called the **Plough** – ties with **Orion** as being the most famous constellation. Orion's fame is clear to see: its bril-liant stars make up a very powerful image of a giant dominating the sky. In con-trast, the stars of the Plough are fainter, and most people today have probably never seen an old-fashioned horse-drawn plough, from which the constellation takes its name. In fact, some children call it 'the saucepan', while in America it's known as the Big Dipper.

But the Plough is the first star-pattern that most people learn. There are two reasons. First, the two end stars of the 'bowl' of the Plough point directly towards the Pole Star, also known as **Polaris**. The Pole Star lies almost direct-ly above the Earth's North Pole. As the Earth spins on its axis, most stars rise and set, whereas Polaris stays still because we are actually rotating *under* it. Locating Polaris is a sure way to find the direction of north. The second reason for the Plough's popularity is that it never sets as seen from northern latitudes, making it a very familiar sight.

▼ *The sky at 10 pm in mid-March, with Moon-positions marked at intervals of three days and at full Moon. The positions of the stars are also correct for*

*I pm at the beginning of March,
nd 10 pm at the end of the
onth (after BST begins).The
lanets move slightly relative to
e stars during the month.*

WEST

The seven stars of the Plough are quite a rarity: unlike most constellations, several of the stars lie at the same distance from the Earth and were born together. The middle five stars are all moving in the same direction (along with brilliant **Sirius**, which is also a member of the group). Over thousands of years, the shape of the Plough will gradually change, as the two 'end' stars go off on their own paths.

PLANETS ON VIEW

It is rumoured that Nicolas Copernicus – the cleric who in 1543 controversially suggested that the planets orbited the Sun – never saw the planet **Mercury**. It's the closest planet to the Sun and is only visible at sunrise and sunset. From Copernicus' native Poland, it was always drowned in low-lying mists. This month there's a chance to out-do Copernicus, with Mercury putting on its best evening show of the year. From 10 to 16 March, Mercury sets at around 7.45 pm – almost two hours after the Sun. At magnitude –0.1, it is as bright as the brightest stars.

Saturn is still prominent in the evening skies, shining at magnitude 0.0 and setting at around 4 am.

Jupiter (magnitude –2.4) is starting to make its presence felt in the southeastern sky, in the constellation of Virgo. The giant planet rises at 8.30 pm at the beginning of March, and 7.30 pm at the end of the month.

Mars is in the constellation of Sagittarius. It rises at approximately 4 am in March, just as morning twilight

MOON			
	Date	Time	Phase
Jupiter	3	5.40 pm	Last Quarter
Saturn	10	9.13 am	New Moon
Moon	17	7.21 pm	First Quarter
	25	9.02 pm	Full Moon

March's Object Praesepe
March's Picture

EAST

15

starts. The Red Planet continues to brighten steadily, passing magnitude +1.0 on 22 March.

Venus, along with the outer planets **Uranus** and **Neptune**, lies too close to the Sun to be visible this month.

MOON

In the morning twilight of 6 March, you'll catch the thin crescent Moon lying below Mars. After it passes the Sun, the thin waxing crescent appears next to Mercury on the evening of 11 March. On 19 March, the Moon – just past first quarter – forms a lovely group with Saturn and the twin stars of Castor and Pollux, in Gemini. On 26 March, the Moon lies between brilliant Jupiter and Spica, Virgo's brightest star.

SPECIAL EVENTS

20 March, 12.33 pm: The Vernal Equinox marks the beginning of spring, as the Sun moves up to shine over the northern hemisphere. At the Equinox, day and night are exactly equal in length, as the Sun is positioned over the equator. From now until the Summer Solstice, the nights will grow shorter and the days longer.

27 March, 1.00 am: British Summer Time starts – don't forget to put your clocks forward by one hour (the mnemonic is 'Spring forward, Fall back').

◉ Viewing tip

This is the time of year to tie down your compass points – the directions of north, south, east and west – as seen from your observing site. North is easy – just find Polaris, the Pole Star, as we describe in March's constellation. But the useful extra in March is the Spring (or Vernal) Equinox, when the Sun hovers over the equator. This means that it rises due east, and sets due west. At noon, the Sun is always due south. So remember these positions relative to a tree or house around your horizon.

◄ *Damian Peach of Loudwater, Buckinghamshire, UK, captured this dramatic image of Saturn using a 250mm Schmidt-Cassegrain telescope equipped with a CCD (charge-coupled device).*

MARCH'S OBJECT

Between Gemini and Leo lies the faint zodiacal constellation of Cancer, the Crab. You'd be hard pressed to see it from a city, but try to focus on the central triangle of stars, and then look inside. With the unaided eye, you can see a misty patch. This is **Praesepe**, a dense group of stars also known as the Beehive Cluster. If you train binoculars on it, you'll understand how it got its name – it really does look like a swarm of bees.

Praesepe lies over 500 light years away, and contains some 300 stars, all of which were born together. Galileo, in 1610, was the first to recognize it as a star cluster. But the ancient Chinese astronomers obviously knew about it, naming the cluster *Tseih She Ke*, meaning 'the Exhalation of Piled-up Corpses'!

MARCH'S PICTURE

Saturn's rings are so wide that they would stretch almost all the way from the Earth to the Moon. But they're incredibly thin – less than a mile in thickness. Although they look solid, the rings are made of millions of chunks of ice, ranging in size from hailstones to office blocks.

MARCH'S TOPIC
Double stars

The Sun is an exception among stars in having singleton status. More than half the stars you see in the sky are double stars, or binaries. Look no further than the Plough for a beautiful naked-eye example: the penultimate star in the Plough's handle (at the bend) is clearly double.

Mizar (the brighter star) and its fainter companion Alcor have often been named 'the horse and rider'. Until recently, there was dispute as to whether they were really in orbit around one another, or just stars that happened to lie in the same direction. Now, the sensitive Hipparcos satellite has pinned down their distances to 78.1 light years (Mizar) and 81.1 light years (Alcor). Although this is a gap of three light years, errors in measurement could mean that the separation is only 0.7 light years, meaning that the two stars form a double-star system. Mizar itself turns out to be a very close double, which in turn is orbited by *another* close double star, making it a quintuple star-group.

There's a down side, however, to double or multiple star systems. The complex gravity of their interactions makes it hard to keep a planet in a stable orbit, thus diminishing the chances of life emerging.

SUNRISE AND SUNSET

Date	Rise (am)	Set (pm)
1	6.46	5.41
2	6.44	5.43
3	6.41	5.45
4	6.39	5.46
5	6.37	5.48
6	6.35	5.50
7	6.33	5.52
8	6.30	5.53
9	6.28	5.55
10	6.26	5.57
11	6.24	5.58
12	6.22	6.00
13	6.19	6.02
14	6.17	6.04
15	6.15	6.05
16	6.12	6.07
17	6.10	6.09
18	6.08	6.10
19	6.06	6.12
20	6.03	6.14
21	6.01	6.16
22	5.59	6.17
23	5.57	6.19
24	5.54	6.21
25	5.52	6.22
26	5.50	6.24
27	6.47	7.26
28	6.45	7.27
29	6.43	7.29
30	6.41	7.31
31	6.38	7.32

Riding high in the south is **Leo**, followed by the spring constellation of **Virgo**. Above them both is the constellation of Coma Berenices – Berenice's Hair – a fuzzy group of faint stars best seen in binoculars. According to legend, Queen Berenice of Egypt donated her lustrous locks to the gods in gratitude for the safe return of her husband from battle; they, in turn, placed her coiffure in the sky.

The sprawling constellation of **Hydra**, the water snake, straggles over 100 degrees – getting on for one-third of the way round the night sky. Its stars are mainly faint, but it is the largest constellation of all. **Saturn** is now starting to make an exit, while **Jupiter** is climbing higher in the eastern sky. Also this month there is an eclipse of the Sun (although visible only from parts of South America and the south Pacific), and the **Lyrids** meteor shower.

APRIL'S CONSTELLATION

Like Orion, **Leo** is one of the rare constellations that looks like its namesake, which in this case is an enormous crouching lion. Leo is one of the oldest constellations, and it commemorates the giant Nemean lion that Hercules slaughtered as the first of his labours. According to legend, the lion's flesh could not be pierced by iron, stone or bronze, so Hercules wrestled with it and choked it to death.

Leo is dominated by his head – the familiar '**sickle**', which looks like a back-to-front question mark. At the base of the sickle is the bright blue-white star **Regulus**, about 85 light years away and 160 times brighter than the Sun. Leo's end is marked by **Denebola**, which in Arabic means 'the lion's tail'. Just underneath the main 'body' of Leo are several spiral galaxies – nearby cities of stars like our own Milky Way. These galaxies can't be seen with the unaided eye, but a sweep along the lion's stomach with a small telescope will reveal them.

▼ The sky at 11 pm in the middle of April, with Moon-positions marked at intervals of three days and at full Moon. The positions of the stars are also

WEST

ORION
Betelgeuse
TAURUS
12 Apr
MN
Algol
AURIGA
Capella
GEMINI
Castor
Pollux
PERSEUS
URSA MAJOR
ANDROMEDA
M81 and M82
Zenith
CASSIOPEIA
The Plough
NORTH
URSA MINOR
Polaris
BOÖTES
CEPHEUS
DRACO
CORONA BOREALIS
Deneb
CYGNUS
Vega
Radiant of Lyrids
LYRA
HERCULES
NE
OPHIUCHUS

EAST

correct for midnight at the beginning of April, and 10 pm at the end of the month. The planets move slightly relative to the stars during the course of the month.

PLANETS ON VIEW

Saturn, in Gemini, is still on view, but is making way for Jupiter in the evening skies. At magnitude +0.1, Saturn sets at around 3 am mid-month.

Jupiter, in the constellation of Virgo, is climbing rapidly in the eastern sky. On 3 April, it will be at opposition – that is, opposite to the Sun in the sky, and highest at midnight – shining brilliantly at a magnitude of −2.5. Planets have no light of their own, unlike stars, and they shine by reflected sunlight, rather like a high-flying aircraft. Jupiter sets in the morning twilight at around 6 am.

Mars, at magnitude +0.8, appears in the morning twilight in the constellation of Capricornus, rising at about 4 am.

Neptune, also in Capricornus, lies close to Mars mid-month, but at magnitude 7.9 you'll need a good telescope to see it in the dawn twilight glow.

Mercury, **Venus** and **Uranus** are lost in the Sun's glare this month.

MOON

On 4 April, the crescent Moon passes below Mars in the morning sky. The evening of 15 April sees the Moon, just shy of first quarter, near Saturn. A week later (22 April), giant planet Jupiter is the bright 'star' near the Moon.

SPECIAL EVENTS

8 April: There is an eclipse of the Sun, visible from the South Pacific and parts of South America, but alas not from Europe. This is a 'hybrid eclipse', which is a very unusual spectacle. It starts and ends as an annular eclipse, where the Moon

WEST

GEMINI
Procyon
CANIS MINOR
Saturn
Castor
Pollux
15 Apr
CANCER
18 Apr
The Sickle
Regulus
LEO
HYDRA
URSA MAJOR
Denebola
21 Apr
CORVUS
SOUTH
Zenith
M51
CANES VENATICI
Arcturus
The Plough
Jupiter
Spica
VIRGO
24 Apr
CORONA BOREALIS
BOÖTES
SERPENS
HERCULES
LIBRA
OPHIUCHUS
SE
EAST

April's Objects
M51, M81 and
M82 Galaxies

April's Picture

Radiant of
Lyrids

Jupiter

Saturn

Moon

MOON		
Date	Time	Phase
2	1.53 am	Last Quarter
8	9.36 pm	New Moon
16	3.40 pm	First Quarter
24	11.09 am	Full Moon

appears too small to cover the Sun, leaving a ring (or *annulus*) visible. In the middle, the eclipse is total, with the Moon completely overlapping the Sun's disc. The reason lies in the relative geometry of the Sun, Moon and the part of the Earth under the eclipse. This month, the Moon is at a distant point in its slightly oval orbit, and is barely capable of hiding the Sun. People in a position to see the beginning or end of the eclipse are well round the curve of the Earth, so the Moon is farther away and appears too small to cover the Sun completely. People in a position to see the middle of the eclipse, however, are closer to the Moon, so it appears bigger and causes a total eclipse, lasting for less than a minute.

22 April: It's the maximum of the **Lyrid** meteor shower, which – by perspective – appear to emanate from the constellation of **Lyra**. The shower, consisting of particles from a comet called Thatcher, is active between 19 and 25 April. Usually it generates a desultory 10 shooting stars an hour, but occasionally we have seen it being a little more generous. This year, moonlight will be a problem, drowning out the fainter meteors.

APRIL'S OBJECTS

A trio of galaxies – two in Ursa Major, and one in neighbouring **Canes Venatici** – called **M81**, **M82** and **M51** are the objects of the month. You can just see each of these galaxies with binoculars, on a really dark night, though a moderately powerful telescope is needed to reveal them in detail. 'M', incidentally, stands for Messier, after an eighteenth-century Parisian astronomer Charles Messier. Desperate to discover comets, he catalogued 103 'fuzzy objects' that misleadingly resembled them. Messier did find a handful of comets, but today he's better remembered for his Messier Catalogue.

M81 is a smooth spiral galaxy, like our Milky Way, with beautiful spiral arms wrapped around a softly glowing core. It's similar in size and mass to our own Galaxy, and lies 11 million light years away.

Lying close to M81 is M82. It is also a spiral galaxy, but one that couldn't be more different. M82 looks a mess, with a huge eruption taking place at its core. This activity is a result of an interaction with M81 some 300 million years ago, when the two galaxies pulled streams of interstellar gas out of one another. Gas clouds are still raining onto M82's core, creating an explosion of star formation. For this reason, M82 is called a 'starburst' galaxy.

M51 – the Whirlpool Galaxy – in Canes Venatici (the hunting dogs) is the epitome of a spiral galaxy, looking for all the world like a firework Catherine Wheel. It was first described by Lord Rosse of Ireland in 1845 as 'spiral convolutions … the most conspicuous of the spiral class'. Lying 30 million light years away, M51 is about the same size as the Milky Way but much brighter. It is even more glorious for being oriented flat-on. M51 is

SUNRISE AND SUNSET		
Date	**Rise (am)**	**Set (pm)**
1	6.36	7.34
2	6.34	7.36
3	6.31	7.37
4	6.29	7.39
5	6.27	7.41
6	6.25	7.42
7	6.23	7.44
8	6.20	7.46
9	6.18	7.47
10	6.16	7.49
11	6.14	7.51
12	6.11	7.52
13	6.09	7.54
14	6.07	7.56
15	6.05	7.57
16	6.03	7.59
17	6.01	8.01
18	5.59	8.02
19	5.56	8.04
20	5.54	8.06
21	5.52	8.07
22	5.50	8.09
23	5.48	8.11
24	5.46	8.12
25	5.44	8.14
26	5.42	8.16
27	5.40	8.17
28	5.38	8.19
29	5.36	8.21
30	5.34	8.22

► *Jupiter, as photographed by Dave Tyler, using a 200 mm reflecting telescope with a ToUcam webcam, from Flackwell Heath, Buckinghamshire, UK.*

accompanied in space by a large companion galaxy, and the two are attached to one another by a stream of stars and gas.

APRIL'S PICTURE

The biggest of all the planets, Jupiter is an amazing sight in a small telescope. Its clouds are drawn out into streaks by the planet's breakneck rotation speed, which also causes Jupiter to bulge like a tangerine around its equator.

APRIL'S TOPIC
Constellations

Leo, our constellation of the month, highlights humankind's obsession to 'join up the dots' in the sky and weave stories around them. But why have we done this? One explanation is that because the constellations on view change during the year as the Earth moves around the Sun, the patterns acted as an *aide memoire* to where we were in our annual cycle. This would have been of especial use to the ancient farming communities.

Another reason is that the stars were a great steer to navigation at sea. In fact, scholars believe that the Greek astronomers 'mapped' their legends onto the sky, so that sailors crossing the Mediterranean would associate certain constellations with their traditional stories.

Not all the world saw the sky through western eyes. The Chinese divided up the sky into a plethora of tiny constellations, containing three or four stars apiece. The Australian Aborigines, in their dark deserts, were so overwhelmed with stars that they made constellations out of the dark places where they couldn't see any stars!

ominating the skies this month are **Leo** and **Virgo**, along with the planet **Jupiter**. Virgo, the second-largest constellation, is shaped like a 'Y'. It's hard to understand how the ancients saw it as a virtuous maiden holding a palm branch in her right hand and an ear of corn in her left. But the astronomers of old knew that the Sun passed the stars of Virgo in the Autumn, and regarded the constellation as a metaphor for a successful harvest.

The summer constellations are starting to put in an appearance, and we are always pleased to see **Arcturus**, the brightest star of **Boötes** because it means that long hot days are on the way. The tiny constellation of **Corona Borealis** follows hot on Bootes' heels. Planetwise, Jupiter still dominates the sky, and **Saturn** is on the way out.

MAY'S CONSTELLATION

Ursa Minor is a miniature version of Ursa Major; in fact, it's known as the 'Little Dipper' in America. It contains the most famous star in the sky – the Pole Star, or **Polaris**. People are always astonished to find that Polaris is relatively obscure, as compared to, say, the dazzling stars of Orion. At magnitude 2.1, it's hardly a star that you'd single out, but it has the distinction of lying – at the moment – almost directly above Earth's North Pole and its axis of rotation. So, the Earth spins 'under' the Pole Star. As a result, Polaris appears to stay almost still in the sky, while all the heavens circle around it. We say 'almost' because the alignment is about one degree off: in AD 2100 Polaris will be at its closest to Earth's axis.

The alignment will deteriorate after 2100 as a result of the Earth's 'wobbling' in space. Our planet is like an old-fashioned spinning top: as it spins, it swings around. The swinging – called *precession* – takes place on the suitably astronomical timescale of nearly 26,000 years, and it means that the Earth's axis slowly points to different points in space. As a result of precession we often don't have a pole star. But a number

▼ *The sky at 11 pm in the middle of May, with Moon-positions marked at intervals of three days and at full Moon. The positions of the stars are also correct for*

WEST

HYDRA
Procyn
CANIS MINOR
Saturn
11 May
GEMINI
AURIGA
Capella
Algol
PERSEUS
NORTH
CASSIOPEIA
ANDROMEDA
CEPHEUS
PEGASUS
NE
Pollux
Castor
CANCER
URSA MAJOR
The Plough
Polaris
Kochab
URSA MINOR
DRACO
Zenith
HERCULES
Vega
LYRA
CYGNUS
Deneb
DELPHINUS
AQUILA
SAGITTA
Altair
14 May
LEO

EAST

midnight at the beginning of May, and 10 pm at the end of the month. The planets move slightly relative to the stars during the month.

of other notable stars have been pole stars in history, and many others will be. For example **Kochab** – also in Ursa Minor – was the pole star during the wars of Troy in 1184 BC. In 14,000 years time, brilliant **Vega**, in **Lyra**, will be our pole star.

PLANETS ON VIEW

Jupiter, at magnitude –2.3, dominates May's skies. It is near the blue-white star **Spica** (Virgo's 'ear of corn'), and Jupiter's yellowish colour makes a marked contrast. It sets at 4 am in mid-May.

Saturn, still in the constellation of **Gemini**, is plunging down into the west, setting at around 1 am. It shines at magnitude +0.2.

Venus is starting to make an appearance in the evening sky, at a magnitude of –3.9. It sets 40 minutes after the Sun at the beginning of May, and 1 hour 20 minutes after sunset by the end of the month.

Mars rises at roughly 3 am mid-month, at a magnitude of +0.6. By now, the lighter nights are catching up with us, and the planet won't be an easy object to observe.

Uranus lies near Mars in Aquarius, but at magnitude 5.8 it is a hundred times fainter. The two planets are closest on the morning of 16 May.

Neptune (magnitude 7.9) in Capricornus is a morning object, rising around 2 am.

Mercury is too close to the Sun to be seen in May.

MOON

In the morning twilight of 2 and 31 May, the 'star' to the left of the waning Moon is the Red Planet, Mars. On the

WEST

CANCER

The Sickle

Regulus

HYDRA

17 May

LEO

URSA MAJOR

CANES VENATICI

Virgo Cluster

Jupiter

20 May

CORVUS

BOÖTES

VIRGO

Spica

HYDRA

CENTAURUS

SOUTH

The Plough

Zenith

Arcturus

CORONA BOREALIS

SERPENS

LIBRA

HERCULES

OPHIUCHUS

SCORPIUS

Antares

23 May

AQUILA

SERPENS

Altair

SE

EAST

May's Object
Virgo Cluster

May's Picture

MOON		
Date	Time	Phase
1	7.27 am	First Quarter
8	9.49 am	New Moon
16	9.59 am	First Quarter
23	9.21 pm	Full Moon
30	12.51 pm	Last Quarter

Jupiter

Saturn

Moon

evenings of 12 and 13 May, the crescent Moon passes Saturn. Jupiter is the bright object near the Moon on 19 May. At 2 am on 21 May, the Moon passes just 1 degree (two Moon-diameters) above Spica, the principal star in the constellation of Virgo.

SPECIAL EVENTS

5 May: It's the maximum of the Eta Aquarid meteor shower. In early May, you might notice a few extra shooting stars. These meteors are tiny pieces of debris shed by Halley's Comet in its 76-year tramp around the Sun. The *radiant* – the point from which the meteors fan out as a result of perspective – is very low in the sky as seen from northern latitudes. People in the Southern Hemisphere, however, may be lucky to see as many as 40 shooting stars an hour.

MAY'S OBJECT

If you have a small telescope, sweep the 'bowl' formed by Virgo's 'Y' shape, and you'll detect dozens of fuzzy blobs. These are just a handful of the thousands of galaxies making up the **Virgo Cluster**. Lying at a distance of 55 million light years, it is our closest giant cluster of galaxies.

Galaxies are gregarious. Thanks to gravity, they like living in groups. Our Milky Way and the neighbouring giant spiral the Andromeda Galaxy live in a small cluster of about 30 smallish galaxies called the Local Group.

◉ **Viewing tip**

Unscrupulous mail-order 'gadget' catalogues often advertise small telescopes that boast huge magnifications. Beware! This is known as 'empty magnification' – blowing up an image that the lens or mirror simply doesn't have the light-grasp to get to grips with. A rule of thumb is to use a maximum magnification no greater than 50 times the diameter of your lens or mirror in inches. So if you have a four-inch reflecting telescope, go no higher than ×200.

◄ *The constellation of Corona Borealis, as photographed by Robin Scagell with a 135 mm telephoto lens on Fuji 1600 slide film, on a driven telescope mount.*

The Virgo Cluster is in a different league: it's like a vast galactic swarm of bees. What's more, its enormous gravity holds sway over the smaller groups around – including our Local Group – to make a cluster of clusters of galaxies, known as the Virgo Supercluster.

The galaxies in the Virgo Cluster are huge. Many of them are spirals like our Milky Way, including the famous 'Sombrero Hat', which looks just like its namesake. Some, however, are even more spectacular: the heavyweight galaxy of the cluster, M87, is a giant elliptical galaxy that emits a jet of gas over 4000 light years long travelling at one-tenth the speed of light.

MAY'S PICTURE

The beautiful little constellation of **Corona Borealis** really does look like a coronet in the sky. Its brightest star, at the base of the circlet, is called Gemma. Shining blue-white, it looks like the jewel in the crown.

SUNRISE AND SUNSET

Date	Rise (am)	Set (pm)
1	5.33	8.24
2	5.31	8.26
3	5.29	8.27
4	5.27	8.29
5	5.25	8.31
6	5.23	8.32
7	5.22	8.34
8	5.20	8.35
9	5.18	8.37
10	5.17	8.38
11	5.15	8.40
12	5.13	8.42
13	5.12	8.43
14	5.10	8.45
15	5.09	8.46
16	5.07	8.48
17	5.06	8.49
18	5.05	8.51
19	5.03	8.52
20	5.02	8.53
21	5.01	8.55
22	4.59	8.56
23	4.58	8.58
24	4.57	8.59
25	4.56	9.00
26	4.55	9.01
27	4.54	9.03
28	4.53	9.04
29	4.52	9.05
30	4.51	9.06
31	4.50	9.07

MAY'S TOPIC
Red giants

Arcturus, the fourth-brightest star in the sky (magnitude –0.04), gladdens our hearts as the harbinger of summer's arrival. But alas, it is a star on the way out. Its orange colour indicates that it's a red giant – a star near the end of its life.

Arcturus is about 30 times wider than the Sun – even though it has the same mass – because it has swollen up in its old age. (A fate that also befalls humans, although the causes are rather different!) Stars generate energy by nuclear fusion: they 'burn' hydrogen into helium in their hot cores. But there's only a finite supply of hydrogen in a star's core. When it runs out – after around ten billion years – the core, made of helium, collapses to a smaller size and gets even hotter. The star is now like an onion, with distinct layers. In the centre, the compressed helium begins its own reactions. In a layer around the core, hydrogen is still turning to helium. These reactions create more heat, causing the outer layers of the star to balloon in size and cool down. This explains the baleful red or orange colour of the star's surface.

Eventually Arcturus, like all red giants, will lose a grip on it atmosphere and jettison it into space. All that's left will be the dying core – a steadily cooling object, about the size of the Earth, called a white dwarf. This fate awaits our Sun, but not for another 5 billion years.

The midsummer month is just about the worst month for astronomy. The days are at their longest, and the nights at their shortest. The hours of darkness depend critically on your latitude. In northern parts of Europe and Canada, it never really gets dark. If you are north of the Arctic Circle (at a latitude of 66.5°N), the Sun doesn't set at all. It just dips down towards the northern horizon, then moves up in the sky again, producing the phenomenon of the Midnight Sun.

At more temperate latitudes, the Sun sets at its most northerly point along the horizon. This unique time of year was picked out by our distant ancestors, who built great monuments like Stonehenge.

JUNE'S CONSTELLATION

Look up to the south, and you'll spot a distinctly orange-coloured star that lords it over a huge area of sky devoid of other bright stars. This is **Arcturus**, the chief star of the constellation **Boötes**, the herdsman. Boötes is shaped rather like a kite. It was mentioned in Homer's *Odyssey*, and its name refers to the fact that Boötes seems to 'herd' the stars that lie in the northern part of the sky. It never sets in our latitudes.

The name of the brightest star, Arcturus, means 'bear-driver'. It appears to drive the Great Bear (**Ursa Major**) around the sky as the Earth rotates. Arcturus is the fourth-brightest star in the whole sky. It's the most brilliant star you can seen on June evenings, as the three brighter stars (Sirius, Canopus and Alpha Centauri) are all below the horizon. Arcturus lies 37 light years from us, and shines 110 times more brilliantly than the Sun. It's a star in old age, expanding into a red giant.

The star at the ten o'clock position from Arcturus is called **Izar**, meaning 'the belt'. Through a good telescope, Izar appears as a gorgeous double star, with one star yellow and the other blue.

▼ The sky at 11 pm in the middle of June, with Moon-positions marked at intervals of three days and at full Moon. The positions of the stars are also

*orrect for midnight at the
eginning of June, and 10 pm at
he end of the month. The planets
nove slightly relative to the stars
during the month.*

WEST

LEO
13 June
VIRGO
Jupiter
16 June
CORVUS
Spica
HYDRA
URSA MAJOR
CANES VENATICI
BOÖTES
Arcturus
Izar
CORONA BOREALIS
SERPENS
LIBRA
The Plough
Zenith
M13
DRACO
Vega
HERCULES
OPHIUCHUS
19 June
SCORPIUS
Antares
SOUTH
LYRA
SAGITTA
CYGNUS
SERPENS
SAGITTARIUS
22 June
SE
PEGASUS
DELPHINUS
Altair
AQUILA
CAPRICORNUS
AQUARIUS
NW

EAST

PLANETS ON VIEW

Venus hangs in the twilight as the glorious Evening Star in the hour or so after sunset. Shining at a brilliant magnitude −3.9, Venus is currently near the far point of its orbit and appears small even in a telescope. During the month, Venus moves steadily upwards in the sky, towards the planet Saturn.

Saturn (magnitude +0.2) lies near Castor and Pollux, the twin stars of Gemini, as it's done all year. Though these three objects are higher in the sky than Venus, they are a good deal fainter, so you'll need a clear northwestern horizon to see them; binoculars will help.

Towards the end of June, Venus, Saturn and **Mercury** take part in a celestial planetary dance. From mid-month, you'll start to see tiny Mercury to the lower right of Venus, shooting upwards towards the brighter planet.

On the evening of 24 June, Venus is flanked by Saturn on the left and brighter Mercury to the right. The next night, Venus passes close to Saturn, with Mercury (at magnitude −0.1) in even closer attendance. The thrilling finale takes place on the evening of 27 June, when Mercury just scrapes below Venus. The separation is 1/20 degree (one-tenth of the Moon's diameter). The sight will be wonderful in a small telescope, with a faint star visible in the same field of view.

Once Venus has set, bright **Jupiter** dominates these short nights, low down in the southwestern sky. It shines at magnitude −2.1. The star to Jupiter's left is **Spica**, the most prominent star of the constellation **Virgo** (the virgin).

Jupiter
Saturn
Moon

June's Object
M13

MOON		
Date	Time	Phase
6	10.56 pm	New Moon
15	2.25 am	First Quarter
22	5.16 am	Full Moon
28	7.27 pm	Last Quarter

Mars rises in the east as the sky begins to brighten again, at around 2 am at the beginning of June, and at 1 am towards the end of the month. During June the planet brightens noticeably, from magnitude +0.3 to –0.1.

Neptune, at magnitude 7.9 in the constellation of Capricornus, rises just after midnight, with **Uranus** (magnitude 5.8) following at about 1 am, in the constellation of Aquarius.

MOON

The narrow crescent Moon lies above the brightest planet Venus, low down in the sunset twilight on 8 June. A day later it's to the right of Saturn. On the evening of 15 June, the bright 'star' near the Moon is the planet Jupiter. The morning of 29 June sees a spectacular close approach between the last quarter Moon and Mars. This will be a gorgeous sight in binoculars at around 2.30 am.

SPECIAL EVENTS

21 June, 7.46 am: It is the Summer Solstice. The Sun reaches its most northerly point in the sky, so 21 June is Midsummer's Day, with the longest period of daylight. At the latitude of London, the Sun is up for 16 hours 39 minutes. Correspondingly, we have the shortest nights.

⊙ *Viewing tip*

This is the month for maximum Sun-viewing, but you must be careful. *Never use a telescope or binoculars to look at the Sun directly* – it could blind you permanently. Fogged film is no safer, because it allows the Sun's infrared (heat) rays to get through. Eclipse goggles are safe, as long as they aren't scratched. The best way to observe the Sun is to project its image through binoculars or a telescope onto a white piece of card.

◀ *The Sun, showing a profusion of sunspots. Robin Scagell obtained this picture by projecting the Sun's image with a 114 mm reflector, and photographing the projected image with a compact digital camera.*

Date	Rise (am)	Set (pm)
1	4.49	9.08
2	4.48	9.10
3	4.48	9.11
4	4.47	9.12
5	4.46	9.12
6	4.46	9.13
7	4.45	9.14
8	4.45	9.15
9	4.44	9.16
10	4.44	9.17
11	4.44	9.17
12	4.43	9.18
13	4.43	9.19
14	4.43	9.19
15	4.43	9.20
16	4.43	9.20
17	4.43	9.21
18	4.43	9.21
19	4.43	9.21
20	4.43	9.21
21	4.43	9.22
22	4.43	9.22
23	4.44	9.22
24	4.44	9.22
25	4.44	9.22
26	4.45	9.22
27	4.45	9.22
28	4.46	9.22
29	4.46	9.22
30	4.47	9.21

SUNRISE AND SUNSET

JUNE'S OBJECT

At the darkest part of a June night, you may spot a faint fuzzy patch way up high in the south. Through binoculars, it appears as a gently glowing ball of light. With a telescope, you can glimpse its true nature: a cluster of almost a million stars, swarming together in space.

This wonderful object is known as **M13**, because it was the thirteenth entry in the catalogue of fuzzy objects recorded by the eighteenth-century French astronomer Charles Messier. We now classify M13 as a *globular cluster*. These great round balls of stars are among the oldest objects in our Galaxy, dating back to its birth some 13 billion years ago.

In 1974, radio astronomers sent a message towards M13, hoping to inform the inhabitants of any planet there of our existence. There's only one problem: M13 lies so far away that we won't receive a reply until AD 52,200!

JUNE'S PICTURE

Sunspots are regions where the Sun's turbulent, gaseous surface is cooler; in these areas the Sun's energy is dammed by powerful magnetic fields. But 'cooler' is relative. The Sun's shining disc is at a temperature of 5500°C, while the sunspots are a 'mere' 4500°C!

JUNE'S TOPIC
The Summer Solstice

Midsummer's Day is not just a date for astronomers' diaries. On the morning of 21 June, thousands of new-agers, druids and latter-day pagans converge on Stonehenge to celebrate midsummer.

Around 3000 BC, the Neolithic farmers of Salisbury Plain carefully observed the exact position on the horizon where the Sun rose on Midsummer's Day – its northernmost rising point of the year. At the time, they dug a huge circular enclosure with a gap in the direction of midsummer sunrise.

Two hundred years later they erected the stone that now marks sunrise – the rough-hewn Heel Stone. It was another 600 years before they erected the great standing stones that make up Stonehenge itself.

Was this the world's first solar observatory, staffed with astronomers keeping a watchful eye on the Sun, and perhaps the Moon? Or was it more symbolic – a great temple to the Sun god? At the moment, no-one knows. But we can say – as two people who have been privileged to watch sunrise from the centre of Stonehenge – that our ancestors certainly knew how to create a truly awesome spectacle!

It's a month of big sprawling faint constellations, studded with a few brilliant jewels of first-magnitude stars. Unlike the obvious star-patterns of winter, such as Orion and Gemini, the summer constellations require a bit more patience to work out.

The easiest way to find your way around the summer sky is to use the brightest stars as signposts. Over in the west is the great Summer Triangle. Its corners are marked by **Vega** (top right), **Deneb** (top left) and **Altair** (bottom) – the brightest stars of their respective constellations, **Lyra** (the lyre), **Cygnus** (the swan) and **Aquila** (the eagle).

Well to the right of Vega is the slightly brighter **Arcturus**, in kite-shaped **Boötes** (see June). Between these two first-magnitude stars lie the hour-glass-shaped constellation of **Hercules** and the distinctive circlet of stars making up **Corona Borealis** (the northern crown). Below Hercules, a large ring of stars forms the body of **Ophiuchus**, the serpent-bearer, who is wrestling with the snake **Serpens**. The head of the snake pokes up from the stars of Ophiuchus towards Corona Borealis.

JULY'S CONSTELLATION

In the deep south of the sky this month lies a baleful red star. This is **Antares** – 'the rival of Mars' – and in its ruddiness it surpasses the famed Red Planet. To ancient astronomers, Antares marked the heart of **Scorpius**, the celestial scorpion.

According to Greek myth, the summer constellation of Scorpius is intimately linked with the winter star pattern of Orion. The mighty hunter Orion boasted that he could kill every creature that lived. In retaliation, the Earth-goddess Gaia created a mighty scorpion that rose behind Orion, and delivered a fatal sting. The gods immortalized these two opponents as star patterns, and placed them at opposite ends of the sky so that Orion sets as Scorpius rises.

▼ The sky at 11 pm in the middle of July, with Moon-positions marked at intervals of three days and at full Moon. The positions of the stars are also

WEST
VIRGO
LEO
The Sickle
CANES VENATICI
BOÖTES
The Plough
URSA MAJOR
HERCULES
AURIGA
DRACO
Zenith
URSA MINOR
Polaris
Capella
NORTH
CASSIOPEIA
CEPHEUS
Deneb
CYGNUS
PERSEUS
Algol
PEGASUS
Square of Pegasus
TRIANGULUM
ANDROMEDA
PISCES
NE
EAST

orrect for midnight at the
beginning of July, and 10 pm at
the end of the month. The planets
move slightly relative to the stars
during the month.

Scorpius is one of the few constellations to look like its name-sake, though from far northern latitudes we only see the upper half. To the top right of Antares, a line of stars marks the scorpion's forelimbs. Originally, the stars we now call **Libra** (the scales) were the scorpion's claws. Below Antares, the scorpion's body stretches down into a fine curved tail (below the horizon on the chart), and a deadly sting.

Scorpius is a treasure-trove of astronomical goodies. There are several lovely double stars, including Antares: its faint companion looks greenish in contrast to Antares' strong red hue. To the right of Antares, binoculars reveal the fuzzy patch of **M4**, a globular cluster made of tens of thousands of stars. M4 is one of the nearest of these giant clusters, at 'just' 7200 light years away.

The 'sting' of Scorpius contains three fine star clusters – M6, M7 and NGC 6231 – so near to us that we can see them with the naked eye; a telescope reveals their stars clearly.

PLANETS ON VIEW

Brilliant **Venus** (magnitude –3.9) is lurking low down in the west, in the evening twilight. On 22 July, Venus passes Regulus – the brightest star in Leo (the lion).

Mercury lies just to the left of Venus at the start of the month, but is only 1/40 as bright; check it out with binoculars or a small telescope.

Jupiter lies to the upper left of Venus, among the stars of Virgo (the virgin), shining at magnitude –1.9. It sets at around 1 am at the beginning of July, and at 11 pm by the end of the month.

WEST

12 July · Jupiter · Spica · VIRGO · 15 July · LIBRA · SM · M4 · SCORPIUS · Antares · 18 July · BOÖTES · Arcturus · CORONA BOREALIS · SERPENS · OPHIUCHUS · SERPENS · SAGITTARIUS · SOUTH · DRACO · Zenith · Vega · LYRA · Ring Nebula · HERCULES · SAGITTA · Deneb · CYGNUS · Altair · AQUILA · CAPRICORNUS · 21 July · DELPHINUS · PEGASUS · Neptune · AQUARIUS · SE · Uranus · PISCES · 24 July

EAST

		MOON		
	Jupiter	**Date**	**Time**	**Phase**
	Uranus	6	1.03 pm	New Moon
	Neptune	14	4.23 pm	First Quarter
	Moon	21	12.03 pm	Full Moon
		28	4.22 am	Last Quarter

⊕ Globular cluster

□ July's Object Ring Nebula

Mars rises in the east, in the constellation of Pisces, as Jupiter sets. The Earth is gradually catching up with the slower moving Red Planet, and so Mars is growing bigger and brighter in the sky. By the end of July, Mars' brightness will reach magnitude –0.5, more brilliant than any of the stars we can see this month.

Uranus (magnitude 5.8), in the constellation of Aquarius, and its outer neighbour **Neptune**, at magnitude 7.8 in Capricornus, are both above the horizon for all the hours of darkness.

Saturn is too close to the Sun to be seen this month.

MOON

In the evening twilight of 8 July, look low in the northwest to see a very narrow crescent Moon above brilliant Venus; with binoculars, you may also spot Mercury below Venus. Jupiter lies near the Moon on 13 July. On the night of the 27/28 July, the last quarter Moon passes Mars.

SPECIAL EVENTS

4 July: Earth is at aphelion, its farthest point from the Sun, at a distance of 152 million km (94.5 million miles).

JULY'S OBJECT

Tucked into the small constellation of Lyra (the lyre) – near the brilliant star Vega – lies a strange celestial sight. It was first spotted by French astronomer Antoine Darquier in 1779, who described it as 'a very dull nebula, but perfectly outlined; as large as Jupiter and looks like a fading planet'. Under higher

> ◉ *Viewing tip*
> This is the month when you really need a good, unobstructed view to the southern horizon, to make out the summer constellations of Scorpius and Sagittarius. They never rise high in temperate latitudes, so make the best of a southerly view – especially over the sea – if you're away on holiday. A good southern horizon is also best for views of the planets, because they rise highest when they're in the south.

◀ *Noctilucent clouds, as photographed by Robin Scagell from Ickenham, Middlesex, UK in summer. These high-altitude clouds – around 80 km (50 miles) high – are visible only near midsummer towards the north, well after sunlight has gone from normal twilight clouds. This 5-second exposure was taken on ISO 400 film, with a camera fixed on a tripod.*

magnification, it appears as a bright ring of light with a dimmer centre, which explains its usual name of the **Ring Nebula**.

You can make out the Ring Nebula with even a small telescope, though it's so compact that you'll need a magnification of over $\times 50$ to distinguish it from a star.

The Ring Nebula is the remains of a dying star; it is a cloud of gas lit up by the original star's incandescent core. For centuries, astronomers assumed that the Ring Nebula was a sphere of gas, but the Hubble Space Telescope found that it's actually barrel-shaped. It looks like a ring to us because we happen to view the barrel end-on. Aliens observing the Ring Nebula from another perspective would undoubtedly call it something different!

JULY'S PICTURE

Noctilucent clouds can appear quite ghostly, shining with a distinct bluish glow. They are thought to be caused by fine dust from meteor particles in the upper atmosphere reflecting sunlight.

SUNRISE AND SUNSET

Date	Rise (am)	Set (pm)
1	4.48	9.21
2	4.48	9.21
3	4.49	9.20
4	4.50	9.20
5	4.51	9.19
6	4.52	9.19
7	4.53	9.18
8	4.54	9.17
9	4.54	9.17
10	4.56	9.16
11	4.57	9.15
12	4.58	9.14
13	4.59	9.13
14	5.00	9.12
15	5.01	9.11
16	5.02	9.10
17	5.03	9.09
18	5.05	9.08
19	5.06	9.07
20	5.07	9.06
21	5.09	9.05
22	5.10	9.03
23	5.11	9.02
24	5.13	9.01
25	5.14	8.59
26	5.16	8.58
27	5.17	8.56
28	5.18	8.55
29	5.20	8.53
30	5.21	8.52
31	5.23	8.50

JULY'S TOPIC
Deep Impact!

If all goes according to plan, this 4 July will be lit up by fireworks on a scale never before attempted, as the American spacecraft Deep Impact blasts the solid core of comet Tempel 1.

Like all comets, Tempel 1 consists of a solid icy core, which steams as it approaches the Sun's heat to produce a gaseous head and long glowing tail. Deep Impact – due for launch on 30 December 2004 – is targeted to collide with the icy nucleus. On 3 July, the spacecraft will release a lump of copper weighing over one-third of a ton, heading towards the comet at 37,000 km/h (23,000 mph). The mother-craft will then alter its path, so it can safely observe the resulting impact.

On 4 July, the projectile will smash into the comet nucleus, with an energy equivalent to 4.8 tons of TNT. It should blast out a crater as big as a football pitch, and seven storeys deep. It will be a spectacular sight as viewed from the mother-craft. Watching from Earth with binoculars, you should see the comet brighten dramatically: it may even burst into naked eye view.

It's not just about spectacle, of course. This is a unique chance to find out what's inside a comet. By shattering the comet's crust, and ejecting its internal matter, astronomers can examine the raw material of the Solar System, including the planets. Deep-frozen in the comet's core may be the raw materials of life itself.

Friends have often said to us 'The sky is so amazing in the south of France: you get to see so many shooting stars.' And we reply 'So mid-August is the time you regularly take your summer holidays.' To their surprise, we are invariably right!

It doesn't take a Sherlock Holmes to make this deduction. Sure, the dark skies of southern France do help in seeing what's going on in the sky. But there's only one time of year – outside deep winter – when the sky is full of shooting stars: August is the meteor-month.

If you are in southern latitudes, the other stunning sight of August is the softly glowing Milky Way – looking like luminous clouds down on the southern horizon. Here, we are looking towards the centre of the Galaxy in which we live – the strange downtown regions of our 'star-city' of some 200 billion stars.

AUGUST'S CONSTELLATION

Low down in the south, you'll find the constellation of **Sagittarius**, shaped rather like a teapot, with the handle to the left and the spout to the right.

To the ancient Greeks, this star-pattern represented an archer, with the torso of a man and the body of a horse. The 'handle' of the teapot represents his upper body; the curve of three stars to the right his bent bow; while the end of the spout is the point of the arrow, aimed at **Scorpius**, the fearsome celestial scorpion.

Sagittarius is rich with nebulae and star clusters. If you have a clear night (preferably from a southern latitude), sweep Sagittarius with binoculars for some fantastic sights. Above the spout lies the wonderful Lagoon Nebula (**M8**) – visible to the naked eye on clear nights. This is a region where stars are being born. Between the Teapot and the neighbouring constellation **Aquila**, you'll see a bright patch of stars in the Milky Way, catalogued as **M24**. Raise your binoculars higher to spot another star-forming region, the Omega Nebula (**M17**).

▼ The sky at 11 pm in the middle of August, with Moon-positions marked at intervals of three days and at full Moon. The positions of the stars are also *correct for midnight at the beginning of August, and 10 pm at the end of the month. The planets move slightly relative to the stars during the month.*

Finally, on a very dark night you might spot a fuzzy patch, above and to the left of the Teapot's lid. This is the globular cluster **M22**, a swarm of almost a million stars that lies 10,000 light years away.

PLANETS ON VIEW

Venus is brilliant in the evening twilight, setting about an hour after the Sun. It shines brighter than any star, at magnitude –3.9.

Jupiter (the second-brightest planet, at magnitude –1.8) is now sinking into the twilight glow, after having dominated the evening sky for so many months. It sets just before 11 pm at the beginning of August, and at 9 pm at the month's end, when it bears down on Venus.

Mars, moving rapidly through Aries, rises at around 11.30 pm at the start of the month, and 10 pm at the end of August. As the Earth approaches the Red Planet, it brightens substantially from magnitude –0.5 to –1.0.

Saturn rises at about 3.30 am towards the end of the month. It lies in the constellation of Cancer.

Neptune reaches opposition on 8 August, at magnitude 7.8. It lies in Capricornus. You'll need a good telescope to spot its largest moon, Triton (magnitude 13).

Uranus is in the neighbouring constellation of Aquarius, at magnitude 5.7.

Mercury is lost in the Sun's glare in August.

MOON

The evening of 7 August sees the crescent Moon to the right of brilliant Venus, an hour or so after sunset. On the evenings

WEST

EAST

SOUTH

CORONA BOREALIS
SERPENS
LIBRA
SCORPIUS
13 Aug
OPHIUCHUS
HERCULES
SERPENS
M24
M17
M8
DRACO
Vega
LYRA
SAGITTA
M22
SAGITTARIUS
16 Aug
Zenith
Deneb
CYGNUS
Altair
AQUILA
ANDROMEDA
North America Nebula
DELPHINUS
Neptune
CAPRICORNUS
Square of Pegasus
PEGASUS
Uranus
19 Aug
PISCIS AUSTRINUS
AQUARIUS
PISCES
22 Aug
CETUS

| | | Mars |
| Uranus |
| August's Object Delta Cephei | | Neptune |
| August's Picture |
| Radiant of Perseids | | Moon |

| **MOON** | | |
Date	Time	Phase
5	4.08 am	New Moon
13	3.42 am	First Quarter
19	6.57 pm	Full Moon
26	4.21 pm	Last Quarter

of 9 and 10 August, it lies near the second-brightest planet, Jupiter. The Moon passes Mars on the night of 24/25 August.

SPECIAL EVENTS

12/13 August: This is the maximum of the **Perseid** meteor shower. The year's most reliable display of shooting stars, it conveniently takes place during the summer, when it's not too uncomfortable to stay up late under the stars.

Every August, the Earth runs into fragments of dust from comet Swift–Tuttle. The comet dust impacts our atmosphere at 210,000 km/h (132,000 mph) and burns up in a streak of light. Because of perspective, the meteors all seem to diverge from the same part of the sky – the meteor *radiant* – which lies in the constellation Perseus.

You'll see Perseid meteors for several nights around the time of maximum. But the best show will come on the night of 12/13 August, after the Moon has set (at around 11.45 pm).

AUGUST'S OBJECT

At first glance, the star **Delta Cephei** – in the constellation representing King Cepheus – does not seem to merit any special attention. A yellowish star of magnitude 4, it is visible to the naked eye, but not prominent. However, this star holds the key to the size of the Universe.

◉ *Viewing tip*

Have a Perseids party! You don't need any optical equipment – in fact, telescopes and binoculars will restrict your view of the meteor shower. The ideal viewing equipment is your unaided eye, plus a sleeping bag and a lounger on the lawn. If you want to make measurements, a stopwatch and clock are good for timings, while a piece of string will help to measure the length and direction of the meteor trail.

◀ *The North America Nebula in Cygnus, photographed by Michael Stecker with a 125 mm refractor. Two one-hour exposures were taken on hypered ISO 400 print film.*

Check the brightness of the star carefully over days and weeks, and you'll see that its brightness changes regularly, from 3.6 (brightest) to 4.3 (faintest), every 5 days 9 hours. This variation is a result of the star literally swelling and shrinking in size, from 32 to 35 times the Sun's diameter.

Astronomers have found that stars like this – known as *Cepheid variables* – show a link between their period of variation and their intrinsic luminosity. By observing the star's period and brightness, astronomers can work out a Cepheid's distance. Using the Hubble Space Telescope, astronomers have now measured Cepheids in the Virgo Cluster of galaxies, which lies 55 million light years away.

AUGUST'S PICTURE

It's obvious how the **North America Nebula** got its name! It is a region where stars are being born, and there is more star-birth on the way. The black region making up the 'Gulf of Mexico' is a cloud of dark material which will condense into stars over the next few millions of years.

SUNRISE AND SUNSET

Date	Rise (am)	Set (pm)
1	5.24	8.49
2	5.26	8.47
3	5.27	8.45
4	5.29	8.44
5	5.30	8.42
6	5.32	8.40
7	5.34	8.38
8	5.35	8.36
9	5.37	8.35
10	5.38	8.33
11	5.40	8.31
12	5.41	8.29
13	5.43	8.27
14	5.45	8.25
15	5.46	8.23
16	5.48	8.21
17	5.49	8.19
18	5.51	8.17
19	5.52	8.15
20	5.54	8.13
21	5.56	8.11
22	5.57	8.09
23	5.59	8.07
24	6.00	8.04
25	6.02	8.02
26	6.04	8.00
27	6.05	7.58
28	6.07	7.56
29	6.08	7.54
30	6.10	7.51
31	6.12	7.49

AUGUST'S TOPIC
Centre of the Galaxy

The Milky Way stretches all the way around our sky, as a gently glowing band. In reality, our Galaxy is a spiral shape comprising some 200 billion stars, with the Sun about halfway out. The centre of the Milky Way lies in the direction of the constellation Sagittarius. But our view of the galactic centre is obscured by great clouds of dark dust that block the view for even the most powerful telescopes.

Now, however, instruments observing at wavelengths other than that of visible light have lifted the veil on the Galaxy's heart. Infrared telescopes can see the heat radiation from stars and gas clouds at the galactic centre. These objects are speeding around so fast that they must be in the grip of something with fantastically strong gravity. In 2002, a team of astronomers at the European Southern Observatory, in Chile, discovered a star orbiting the Galaxy's centre at over 18 million km/h (12 million mph). In the meantime, radio astronomers have found that the Galaxy's exact heart is marked by a tiny source of radiation.

Putting all these observations together, astronomers have concluded that the core of the Milky Way must contain a heavyweight black hole as massive as 2.6 million Suns. When a speeding star comes too close to this invisible monster, it's ripped apart. There's a final shriek from the star's gases – producing the observed radio waves – before they fall into the black hole, and disappear from our Universe.

This month we might be treated to the warm sunny days of an Indian summer, but to astronomers winter actually begins on 22 September. On the Autumn Equinox, the Sun crosses the Equator and moves down to the southern hemisphere of the sky.

In the night sky, the Summer Triangle – **Deneb**, **Vega** and **Altair** – is shifting over to the west. Rising in the east are the autumn star patterns, commencing with the distinct **Square of Pegasus** (the flying horse), followed by the princess **Andromeda**, her mother **Cassiopeia** and her suitor **Perseus**.

SEPTEMBER'S CONSTELLATION

Delphinus, the celestial dolphin, is small but perfectly formed. It is outlined by four stars making a lopsided rectangle, with an extra star forming his tail. To find this constellation, locate the Summer Triangle of the bright stars Vega, Deneb and Altair, then look to the upper left of Altair.

The constellation of Delphinus immortalizes humanity's long relationship with the most intelligent marine life on our planet. According to one myth, the dolphin acted as go-between when the sea-god Poseidon (Neptune) was courting his wife, the sea-nymph Amphitrite. In another story, the dolphin rescued the musician Arion when he was thrown overboard by sailors intent on stealing his wealth.

The two stars to the right of the rectangle are called Sualocin and Rotanev. These strange-looking names represent self-promotion by a nineteenth-century Italian astronomer Niccolo Cacciatore. In Latin, his name becomes Nicolaus Venator: try spelling this backwards!

The top-left star of Delphinus, **Gamma Delphini**, is a lovely double star when you observe it with a reasonable telescope.

▼ The sky at 11 pm in the middle of September, with Moon-positions marked at intervals of three days and at full Moon. The positions of the stars are also

WEST

NW

Arcturus

CORONA BOREALIS

SERPENS

OPHIUCHUS

CANES VENATICI

BOÖTES

HERCULES

SERPENS

The Plough

DRACO

Vega

LYRA

CYGNUS

URSA MAJOR

URSA MINOR

Polaris

Deneb

Zenith

CEPHEUS

NORTH

CASSIOPEIA

ANDROMEDA

TRIANGULUM

ARIES

Capella

PERSEUS

Algol

Mars

Pleiades

AURIGA

24 Sept

NE

PERSEUS

Aldebaran

TAURUS

21 Sept

EAST

correct for midnight at the beginning of September, and 10 pm at the end of the month. The planets move slightly relative to the stars during the month.

PLANETS ON VIEW

The month begins with a close approach between the two most brilliant planets – **Venus** and **Jupiter** – although the action takes place low down in the evening twilight. At around 7.30 pm on 1 September, you'll see brilliant Venus (at magnitude – 4.0) just above the horizon. Immediately above Venus, separated by just over a degree, lies Jupiter. At magnitude –1.7, it's little more than one-tenth as bright as Venus.

After this close approach, Jupiter disappears into the evening twilight. Venus continues to hug the horizon after sunset, moving gradually to the southwest.

Mars rises at around 10 pm at the beginning of September, over in the east in the constellation of Aries (the ram). It begins the month at magnitude –1.0, and it carries on brightening throughout the month, to reach –1.7. By the end of the September, Mars is brighter than any star and rises at around 8 pm.

Saturn rises at 3 am at the start of the month, and at 1 am by the close of September. At magnitude +0.3, it lies in the constellation Cancer (the crab). Between 12 and 25 September it passes below the star cluster **Praesepe** – a lovely sight in binoculars or a small telescope.

Uranus, at magnitude 5.7, lies in the constellation of Aquarius and reaches opposition on 1 September.

Neptune, in the constellation of Capricornus, is rather fainter (magnitude 7.8).

Mercury lies too close to the Sun to be visible this month.

WEST

SERPENS
OPHIUCHUS
SERPENS
SAGITTARIUS
HERCULES
LYRA
Vega
Albireo
SAGITTA
Gamma
Altair
AQUILA
Deneb
Zenith
CYGNUS
DELPHINUS
Neptune
CAPRICORNUS
CEPHEUS
ANDROMEDA
PEGASUS
Square of Pegasus
Uranus
Helix Nebula
PISCIS AUSTRINUS
GRUS
SOUTH
12 Sept
15 Sept
AQUARIUS
Fomalhaut
TRIANGULUM
PISCES
18 Sept
CETUS
ARIES
Mira
ERIDANUS
TAURUS
SE

EAST

	Mars
	Neptune
	Uranus
	Moon

September's Object
Albireo

September's Picture

MOON		
Date	Time	Phase
3	7.50 pm	New Moon
11	12.39 pm	First Quarter
18	3.05 am	Full Moon
25	7.44 am	Last Quarter

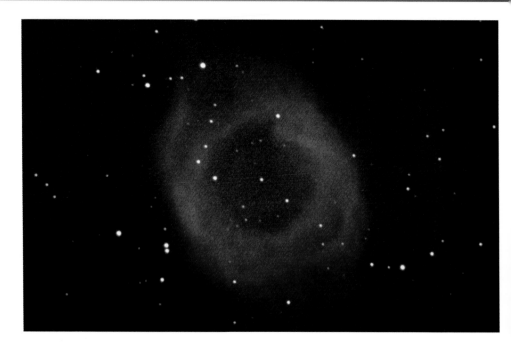

MOON

The month begins with the narrow crescent Moon lying just to the left of Saturn in the dawn twilight. On 7 September, at 8 pm, the Moon's waxing crescent appears low in the evening sky to the west, forming a line with the brightest planets, Venus and Jupiter. On the evening of 21 September, Mars lies near the Moon. On the morning of 28 September, the Moon is close to Saturn.

SPECIAL EVENTS

22 September, 11.23 pm: Today is the Autumn Equinox. The Sun lies above the Equator as it heads southwards in the sky, and day and night are equal in length. Today the Sun rises due east and sets due west, so it's useful if you want to check the cardinal points (north, south, east and west) on your horizon.

SEPTEMBER'S OBJECT

The constellation **Cygnus** represents a soaring swan, her wings outspread as she flies down the Milky Way. The lowest star in Cygnus, marking the swan's head, is **Albireo**. The name looks Arabic, but it actually has no meaning and is merely the result of errors in translation from Greek to Arabic to Latin.

Binoculars reveal that Albireo is actually two stars in one. Use a telescope, and you'll be treated to one of the most glorious sky-sights – a dazzling yellow star teamed with a blue companion.

The yellow star is a giant, near the end of its life: it's 80 times bigger than the Sun, and 1000 times brighter. The fainter blue companion is 'only' 95 times brighter than the Sun.

◉ **Viewing tip**

Try to observe your favourite objects when they're well clear of the horizon. When you look low down, you are seeing through a large thickness of the atmosphere, which is always shifting and turbulent. It's like trying to observe the outside world from the bottom of a swimming pool! This turbulence makes the stars appear to twinkle. Low-down planets also twinkle, but because they subtend tiny discs the twinkling is less marked.

◄ *The Helix Nebula in the constellation of Aquarius is the closest planetary nebula to the Sun. Even so, it's difficult to photograph, being large and comparatively dim. This image was taken by Michael Stecker with a 355 mm Schmidt-Cassegrain telescope at f/6 on ISO 3200 film.*

The spectacular colour contrast is due to the stars' different temperatures. The giant star is slightly cooler than our Sun, and shines with a yellowish glow. The smaller companion is far hotter: it's so incandescent that it shines not merely white-hot, but blue-white.

SEPTEMBER'S PICTURE

The **Helix Nebula** is a star at the end of its life; it has puffed off its outer atmosphere and left its faint nuclear-reactor core behind. In five billion years this fate will befall our Sun.

SEPTEMBER'S TOPIC
Extrasolar planets

For most of the time that we were growing up as astronomers – in fact since the discovery of Pluto in 1930 – the total number of planets known in the entire Universe stood at just nine. But there's been a real revolution in astronomy in the past ten years: the total has now surpassed 130 planets.

The nine original planets – Mercury to Pluto – orbit our own Sun. The new 'extrasolar' planets circle around other stars. It's incredibly difficult to find them, rather like looking for fireflies round a searchlight. But there's now plenty of indirect proof.

The first discovery came in October 1995, when Swiss astronomers Michel Mayor and Didier Queloz found that the faint star 51 Pegasi – just to the right of the great Square of Pegasus – was being pulled backwards and forwards every four days. It had to be the work of a planet, pulling its parent star. Astonishingly, this planet is around the same size as our Solar System's giant, Jupiter, but it is far closer to its star than Mercury. Astronomers call such planets 'hot jupiters'.

A team in California led by Geoff Marcy was already looking for planets, and soon found more. Friendly rivalry between the groups has led to more than 110 more planets being found.

In addition, astronomers have found several more planets by watching for stars to dim in brightness as a planet passes in front of them. One planet has even been discovered because its gravity is bending and focusing the light from a very distant star.

All the extrasolar planets discovered so far are big, like Jupiter or Saturn. Present-day telescopes cannot detect a planet as small as Earth 'out there'. Future space missions will change that. NASA and the European Space Agency are racing to launch a telescope above Earth's distorting atmosphere. It will search for a twin Earth, where life could exist.

SUNRISE AND SUNSET		
Date	Rise (am)	Set (pm)
1	6.13	7.47
2	6.15	7.45
3	6.16	7.42
4	6.18	7.40
5	6.20	7.38
6	6.21	7.36
7	6.23	7.33
8	6.24	7.31
9	6.26	7.29
10	6.28	7.27
11	6.29	7.24
12	6.31	7.22
13	6.32	7.20
14	6.34	7.17
15	6.36	7.15
16	6.37	7.13
17	6.39	7.10
18	6.40	7.08
19	6.42	7.06
20	6.43	7.04
21	6.45	7.01
22	6.47	6.59
23	6.48	6.57
24	6.50	6.54
25	6.52	6.52
26	6.53	6.50
27	6.55	6.47
28	6.56	6.45
29	6.58	6.43
30	7.00	6.41

The event of the month is the eclipse of the Sun on the morning of 3 October, the first to be seen from the UK for over two years. The Sun is roughly half covered by the Moon – and we'll have to wait more than five years before there's a more spectacular eclipse than this one.

The evenings are now drawing in, providing splendid views of the night sky at relatively social hours – especially at the end of the month, when the clocks go back and we lose the summer's extra hour of evening light.

OCTOBER'S CONSTELLATION

High in the north hangs **Cassiopeia**, a star-pattern making the unmistakable shape of a capital 'W' or 'M'. To ancients, this constellation represented Queen Cassiopeia of Ethiopia, who ruled with her husband King Cepheus.

Cassiopeia foolishly boasted that her daughter Andromeda was more beautiful than the sea-nymphs. The sea-god, Poseidon, was so incensed that he sent a ravaging monster (Cetus). It could only be appeased by the sacrifice of Andromeda – but she was rescued by the hero Perseus.

Cepheus, **Andromeda**, **Cetus** and **Perseus** are all visible in the tableau of the heavens this month.

The Chinese saw Cassiopeia as three star-groups, including a mountain path and a chariot. Unusually, the central star in Cassiopeia is known today by its Chinese name of **Tsih** (the whip). This star is unstable in brightness. Some 70,000 times brighter than the Sun, it spins around at breakneck pace flinging out streams of gas.

Cassiopeia has seen two more extreme variable stars – *supernovae*, where an entire star has blown apart. One was seen by the Danish astronomer Tycho Brahe in 1572. The other exploded around 1660 as a surprisingly dim supernova, but its expanding gases form the most prominent radio source in the sky, Cassiopeia A.

▼ The sky at 11 pm in mid-October, with Moon-positions marked at intervals of three days and at full Moon. The star positions are also correct for

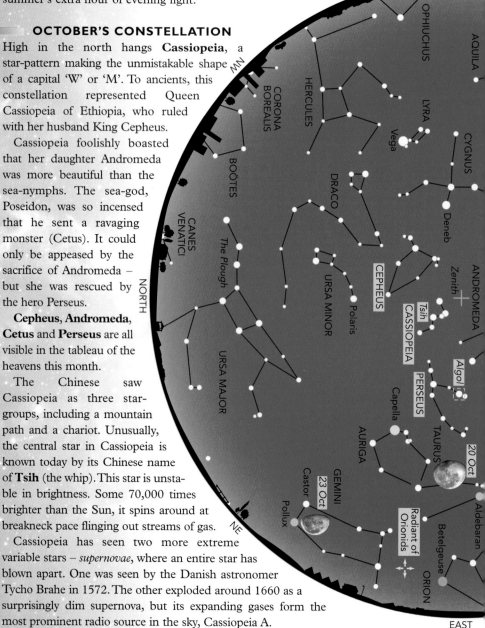

PLANETS ON VIEW

Venus begins the month skulking low in the evening twilight. Look towards the southwest to see this diffident Evening Star setting only an hour after the Sun. By the end of October, it is setting two hours after sunset and shining prominently at magnitude –4.4.

Mars, the Red Planet, is being rapidly caught up by the fast-moving Earth, and its brightness increases spectacularly this month from magnitude –1.7 to –2.3. You'll find Mars on the boundary of the constellations Aries and Taurus, rising in the east at around 8 pm at the start of the month and 5 pm at the end of October (after the end of British Summer Time).

Saturn rises at about 1.30 am at the beginning of October and 10.30 pm by the close of the month. It lies among the stars of Cancer, and shines at magnitude +0.4.

Uranus lies in the constellation of Aquarius. At magnitude 5.8, it is just visible to the naked eye, but easier to pick out in binoculars.

Neptune (magnitude 7.9), in Capricornus, is best seen in a small telescope.

Mercury and **Jupiter** are too close to the Sun to be seen this month.

MOON

On 7 October, the crescent Moon forms a pleasing pair in the evening sky with brilliant Venus. On 18 October the Moon – just past full – lies near Mars. The following night (19/20 October, at around 4 am), the Moon brushes the southern fringes of the **Pleiades**, or Seven Sisters, star cluster – a fascinating sight in binoculars or a small telescope. In the early morning of 25 and 26 October, the Moon lies near Saturn.

midnight at the beginning of October, and 9 pm at the end of the month (after the end of BST). The planets move slightly relative to the stars during the month.

WEST

SERPENS
AQUILA
11 Oct
Ms
Altair
SAGITTA
CYGNUS
DELPHINUS
Deneb
Neptune
AQUARIUS
CAPRICORNUS
Zenith
Andromeda Galaxy
PEGASUS
Uranus
Fomalhaut
CASSIOPEIA
ANDROMEDA
Square of Pegasus
14 Oct
PISCIS AUSTRINUS
SOUTH
PERSEUS
Algol
17 Oct
PISCES
Mira
CETUS
Pleiades
TRIANGULUM
ARIES
Mars
ERIDANUS
Aldebaran
TAURUS
Betelgeuse
ORION
Rigel
SE

EAST

	MOON	
Date	**Time**	**Phase**
3	11.31 am	New Moon
10	8.03 pm	First Quarter
17	1.17 pm	Full Moon
25	2.20 am	Last Quarter

October's Object
October's Picture
Radiant of Orionids

Mars
Uranus
Neptune
Moon

SPECIAL EVENTS

3 October: There is an annular eclipse of the Sun. If you happen to be on the narrow eclipse track – which runs from Madrid through northern and eastern Africa and out into the Indian Ocean – you'll see the Sun appear as a ring of light around the silhouette of the Moon.

From Britain, we'll see a partial solar eclipse. From London, 57% of the Sun is covered, and the eclipse starts at 8.48 am and ends at 11.17 am. If you're in Edinburgh, the eclipse lasts from 8.52 to 11.12 am, with the Sun 47% obscured at maximum.

Observe the eclipse safely! Don't look at the Sun directly, even through sunglasses or fogged film (they don't block the Sun's heat). It is safe to observe though special eclipse goggles (you may have some left over from 1999). But the best way is to project the Sun's image, using a small hole in a piece of cardboard. You can also use binoculars or a small telescope to project an enlarged view of the Sun onto a sheet of white card or paper, but *don't look through the binoculars or telescope*, even for an instant, because they will concentrate the Sun's heat into your eyeball.

17 October: There is an eclipse of the Moon. People in Asia, the Pacific and North America will see 7% of the Moon darkened by the Earth's shadow. Sadly, it can't be seen from the UK.

21 October: It is the maximum of the **Orionid** meteor shower. These meteors are debris from Halley's Comet, burning up in Earth's atmosphere. The area of the sky from where the meteors appear to spray out is called the *radiant*, and it lies in the constellation Orion. But 2005 is not a good year, as moonlight will drown out all but the brightest meteors.

30 October, 2 am: British Summer Time ends. Clocks go backwards by one hour.

OCTOBER'S OBJECT

The star **Algol**, in the constellation Perseus, represents the head of the dreadful Gorgon Medusa. In Arabic, its name means 'the Demon'. Watch Algol carefully and you'll see why. Every 2 days 21 hours, Algol dims in brightness for several hours – to become as faint as the star lying to its lower right (Gorgonea Tertia).

In 1783, a young British amateur astronomer, John Goodricke of York, discovered Algol's regular changes. He proposed that Algol is orbited by a large dark planet that periodically blocks some of its light. We now know that Algol does indeed have a dim companion blocking its brilliant light, but it's a fainter star rather than a planet.

Many of the *minima* of Algol take place during daylight hours; but keep a spot check on Algol over several hours on the nights of 12/13, 15/16, 17/18 and 20/21 October to catch the cosmic wink.

▶ The Andromeda Galaxy, M31, as photographed by Philip Perkins, based in Wiltshire. He took this image with a 400 mm telephoto lens, mounted on a Meade telescope for guidance. In this photograph, M31's two biggest companion galaxies – M32 (top) and NGC 205 (bottom) – flank the giant spiral, which contains 400,000 million stars.

SUNRISE AND SUNSET		
Date	Rise (am)	Set (pm)
1	7.01	6.38
2	7.03	6.36
3	7.05	6.34
4	7.06	6.32
5	7.08	6.29
6	7.10	6.27
7	7.11	6.25
8	7.13	6.23
9	7.15	6.20
10	7.16	6.18
11	7.18	6.16
12	7.20	6.14
13	7.21	6.12
14	7.23	6.09
15	7.25	6.07
16	7.26	6.05
17	7.28	6.03
18	7.30	6.01
19	7.31	5.59
20	7.33	5.57
21	7.35	5.55
22	7.37	5.53
23	7.38	5.51
24	7.40	5.49
25	7.42	5.47
26	7.44	5.45
27	7.45	5.43
28	7.47	5.41
29	7.49	5.39
30	6.51	4.37
31	6.52	4.35

OCTOBER'S PICTURE

The **Andromeda Galaxy** is one of the biggest spiral galaxies known, with nearly twice the number of stars as are in the Milky Way. Unfortunately, it is presented to us at such a shallow angle that it's hard to pick out the spiral arms.

OCTOBER'S TOPIC
Eclipse of the Sun

⊚ **Viewing tip**

At a distance of 2.9 million light years, the Andromeda Galaxy is the farthest object easily visible to the unaided eye. But it's large and extended, and not that easy to spot. The trick is to memorize the star patterns in Andromeda and look slightly to the side of where you expect the galaxy to be. This technique – called 'averted vision' – causes the image to fall on a part of the retina that is more light sensitive than the central part, which is designed to see fine detail.

On our first trip to witness an eclipse of the Sun, from Indonesia in 1988, we were astonished to meet American astronomer Glenn Schneider: in the previous 18 years, he'd seen 10 total eclipses.

That just goes to show that eclipses of the Sun – nature's most awesome spectacle – are not particularly rare. They happen every 16 months on average. You just have to travel to exactly the right place, where the Moon's narrow shadow sweeps across our planet, hiding the Sun's brilliant disc and revealing its eerie faint atmosphere, the corona.

Sometimes, as this month, the Moon lies so far away that it doesn't cover the Sun completely. From the eclipse central line, you'll see a ring (*annulus* in Latin) of the Sun's light around the Moon's silhouette.

The next total solar eclipse is on 29 March next year. It is visible from a line stretching from Nigeria via Libya to Turkey and central Asia. From Britain, we'll see another partial eclipse. The next total eclipse visible from the UK mainland is in September 2090.

It's truly autumn now, and that's reinforced by what we see in the sky. The faint, sprawling constellations of **Pegasus**, **Andromeda**, **Pisces** and **Cetus** make the heavens look lacklustre, reflecting the autumnal landscape here on Earth.

But two planets compensate for the dearth of exciting stars. Both **Venus** and **Mars** are brilliant evening objects, and they are seen at their best this month. There's the added bonus of the **Leonid** meteor shower on 17 November.

NOVEMBER'S CONSTELLATION

It takes considerable imagination to see the line of stars making up Andromeda as a young princess chained to a rock, about to be eaten by a vast sea monster (Cetus) – but that's ancient legends for you. Despite its rather mundane appearance, the constellation Andromeda contains some surprising delights. One is **Almach**, a beautiful double star at the left-hand end of the line. The main star is a yellow supergiant shining 650 times brighter than the Sun; its 5th-magnitude companion is bluish. The two stars are a lovely sight in small telescopes. Almach is actually a quadruple star, and its companion is triple.

The glory of Andromeda is its great galaxy, beautifully placed on November nights. Lying above the line of stars, the **Andromeda Galaxy** (M31) is the most distant object visible to the unaided eye. It lies a mind-boggling 2.9 million light years away, yet it is so vast that it appears nearly six times as big as the full Moon in the sky (although the sky will seldom be clear enough to allow you to see the faint outer spiral arms).

The Andromeda Galaxy is the biggest member of the Local Group, and is estimated to contain over 400 billion stars. It is a wonderful sight in binoculars or a small telescope, and the latter will reveal its two bright companion galaxies – M32 and NGC 205.

▼ The sky at 10 pm in mid-November, with Moon-positions marked at intervals of three days and at full Moon. The star positions are also correct for

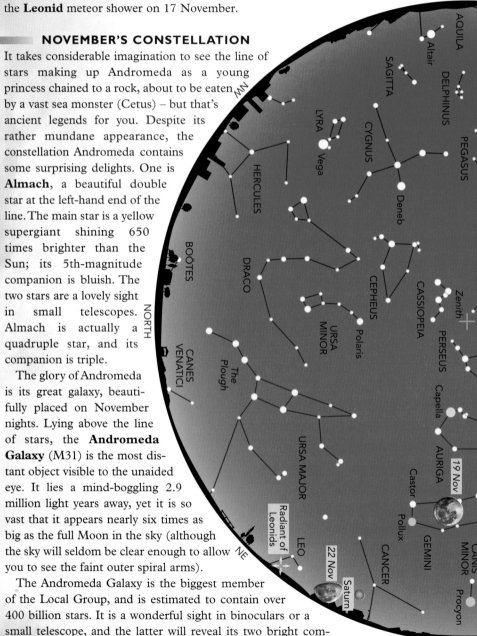

1 pm at the beginning of November, and 9 pm at the end of the month. The planets move slightly relative to the stars during the month.

WEST

AQUILA

DELPHINUS

CYGNUS

CASSIOPEIA

PEGASUS

Square of Pegasus

ANDROMEDA

Andromeda Galaxy

Zenith

Almach

Algol

PERSEUS

Capella

AURIGA

GEMINI

CANIS MINOR

Procyon

CAPRICORNUS

Uranus

10 Nov

AQUARIUS

Fomalhaut

M33

TRIANGULUM

13 Nov

PISCES

ARIES

Mars

Mira

CETUS

Pleiades

Aldebaran

TAURUS

ERIDANUS

16 Nov

Betelgeuse

ORION

Rigel

LEPUS

SOUTH

SE

EAST

PLANETS ON VIEW

Venus, at magnitude –4.6, is putting on a sensational appearance in the evening sky this month, setting at 6.30 pm – more than two hours after the Sun. On 3 November, Venus reaches greatest *elongation*: its maximum distance from the Sun in the sky (see page 54). On 18 November, it passes very close to the star Nunki in Sagittarius.

Mars, in the constellation of Aries, rivals Venus. The Red Planet reaches opposition this month, meaning that it is at its closest point to the Earth and is visible in the sky all night. Mars shines with a distinctly red glow at magnitude –2.4.

Saturn, the ringed planet, is returning to our evening skies, at magnitude +0.2. Mid-month, it rises at around 10 pm, in the constellation of Cancer.

Jupiter, in the constellation of Virgo, rises at around 5 am at a magnitude of –1.7.

Neptune, at magnitude 7.9, lies in the constellation of Capricornus, setting at around 10 pm.

Uranus, at magnitude 5.8, is to be found in the neighbouring constellation of Aquarius. It sets at about midnight.

Mercury is lost in the Sun's glare in November.

MOON

November 5 sees the crescent Moon in the southwest, lying beneath Venus. On the evening of 14 November, the almost full Moon is near Mars. The Moon passes Saturn on the nights of 21 and 22 November. If you're up early on the morning of 29 November, you'll see the Moon's narrow waning crescent close to Jupiter.

| Mars |
| Saturn |
| Uranus |
| Moon |

November's Object M33 Galaxy

November's Picture

Radiant of Leonids

MOON		
Date	**Time**	**Phase**
2	1.26 am	New Moon
9	1.59 am	First Quarter
16	1.01 am	Full Moon
23	10.15 pm	Last Quarter

SPECIAL EVENTS

17 November: This is the maximum of the **Leonid** meteor shower. Unfortunately, it is likely to be a disappointment. The shower has been eagerly awaited in the last few years because it yields literally storms of shooting stars – many thousands an hour. This year, however, is not looking at all encouraging. For a start, Comet Tempel–Tuttle, the parent comet, which sheds its dust to produce the meteors, has moved away from the vicinity of Earth, as have the rich streams of debris that we've encountered recently. Also, the Moon is full on 16 November, so its light will drown out the shooting stars. It is best to expect no more than 10 meteors an hour.

NOVEMBER'S OBJECT

Just below the line of stars making up Andromeda is the galaxy **M33**, in the constellation of Triangulum. Although the Andromeda Galaxy is generally accepted to be the most distant object visible to the unaided eye, some amateur astronomers claim that – under exceptionally clear conditions – M33 can be seen. At magnitude 5.7 (with 6.0 being the naked-eye cut-off), this is plausible. But the light of the galaxy is spread out thinly, so there's very little contrast between the galaxy and the natural light of the night-time sky. At a distance of 3 million light years, this truly would make M33 the farthest object visible to the naked eye.

M33 is a member of our Local Group. It's a spiral galaxy, rather more ragged and unbuttoned than the Milky Way and Andromeda. It's also a lot smaller, being only half the diameter of the Milky Way, at 50,000 light years across. But it makes up for its size by containing one of the biggest star-forming regions known in the Universe. NGC 204 is a huge cloud of gas and dust 1500 light years across (in comparison the Orion Nebula is only 15 light years wide). NGC 204 is already busy creating stars: images from the Hubble Space telescope have revealed over 200 young stars with masses between 15 and 60 times that of the Sun lurking in its mists.

If you want to see M33 properly, you need a telescope. But don't use a high magnification as this will just spread the galaxy out, making it more difficult to see. Use a low magnification on a really transparent night.

NOVEMBER'S PICTURE

The dark markings on **Mars** were once thought to be primitive vegetation, but are now known to be greyish expanses of rocks. Some of the smooth desert-like regions could be the beds of ancient oceans, which may have once harboured life.

SUNRISE AND SUNSET		
Date	Rise (am)	Set (pm)
1	6.54	4.34
2	6.56	4.32
3	6.58	4.30
4	7.00	4.28
5	7.01	4.27
6	7.03	4.25
7	7.05	4.23
8	7.07	4.22
9	7.08	4.20
10	7.10	4.18
11	7.12	4.17
12	7.14	4.15
13	7.15	4.14
14	7.17	4.13
15	7.19	4.11
16	7.20	4.10
17	7.22	4.09
18	7.24	4.07
19	7.26	4.06
20	7.27	4.05
21	7.29	4.04
22	7.30	4.03
23	7.32	4.02
24	7.34	4.01
25	7.35	4.00
26	7.37	3.59
27	7.38	3.58
28	7.40	3.57
29	7.41	3.56
30	7.43	3.56

▶ *Mars, as photographed on 23 August 2003, when it was at almost its closest to Earth for 60,000 years. The region shown is the Sinus Meridiani area, with Solis Lacus at right. This image has south at the top, with the south polar cap very prominent. It was taken by Damian Peach, using a 280-mm Schmidt-Cassegrain telescope and ToUcam.*

◉ **Viewing tip**

Now that the nights are drawing in and becoming darker, it's a good time to pick out faint, fuzzy objects like the Andromeda Galaxy and the Orion Nebula. But don't even think about it near the time of full Moon, as its light will drown them out. The best time to observe such 'deep sky objects' is when the Moon is near to new, or after full. Check the Moon phases timetable in this book.

NOVEMBER'S TOPIC
Venus

Venus is unmissable this month as a stunning 'evening star'. It's the closest planet to the Earth and virtually our twin in size (Venus is a little smaller), but it is a world that has got out of control. Part of the reason for its brilliancy is that it has a thick atmosphere of carbon dioxide, laced with sulphuric acid clouds, which reflects sunlight with considerable attitude. This unpleasant 'air' is so heavy that it exerts a pressure of 90 Earth-atmospheres on the planet. Underneath, it has trapped the heat from sunlight and hundreds of erupting volcanoes to create a world hotter than an oven – one in which the Greenhouse Effect has gone out of control. If you went to Venus you would be roasted, crushed, suffocated and corroded.

This month, however, we'll be staging a return to Venus after over ten years. Europe's Venus Express spaceprobe is due to launch on 1 November. It will reach the planet in only 153 days, and will then spend over a year in orbit examining the planet in detail. Among the mysteries that researchers want to solve is the cause of Venus's volcanic hell, and what lies behind the planet's runaway Greenhouse Effect. It will certainly have lessons to teach us about our own recent climate change.

Winter is with us, and we even have a Christmas Star! Venus is setting at around 6.30 pm, and it looks like a brilliant lantern in the sky – many people will notice it as they do their festive shopping. The other planets on show in the evening are **Mars** and **Saturn**. For those on the morning shift, Jupiter and Mercury are putting in an appearance.

The constellations of winter have returned – as the **Pleiades** climb higher in the sky we contemplate the short days ahead. They are followed by the unmistakeable shape of **Orion**, and – low in the southeast – **Sirius**, the brightest star in the sky.

DECEMBER'S CONSTELLATION

Taurus is very much a second cousin to brilliant Orion, but it is a fascinating constellation nonetheless. It's dominated by **Aldebaran**, the baleful blood-red eye of the celestial bull. At around 68 light years away, and shining with a magnitude of 0.85, Aldebaran is a red giant star, but it is not as extreme as neighbouring **Betelgeuse**. It is around three times heavier than the Sun.

The 'head' of the bull is formed by the **Hyades** star cluster, our 'Object of the month'. The other famous star cluster in Taurus is the far more glamorous Pleiades, whose stars – although farther away than the Hyades – are younger and brighter.

Taurus has two 'horns' – the star El Nath (Arabic for 'the butting one') to the north, and Zeta (which has an unpronounceable Babylonian name meaning 'star in the bull towards the south'). Above this star is a stellar wreck – literally. In 1054, Chinese astronomers witnessed a brilliant 'new star' appear in this spot, which was visible in daytime for weeks. What the Chinese actually saw was an exploding star – a *supernova* – in its death throes. Today, we can see its still-expanding remains as the Crab Nebula (**M1**). It's visible through a medium-sized telescope.

▼ *The sky at 10 pm in the middle of December, with Moon positions marked at intervals of three days and at full Moon. The star positions are also correct for*

50

I pm at the beginning of December, and 9 pm at the end of the month. The planets move slightly relative to the stars during the course of the month.

PLANETS ON VIEW

Venus is the planet of the month, shining brilliantly at magnitude –4.6 in the west and setting at 6.30 pm.

Mars is high in the south, in the constellation of Aries, setting at around 4 am. It starts the month at a brilliant magnitude –1.6, but as the fast-moving Earth pulls away from the Red Planet, it fades to –0.6 by the end of the month.

Saturn is powering up the eastern sky. In the constellation of Cancer, it rises at around 9 pm at the start of the month. By the end of December, it has hurtled forward to 7 pm. Its brightness is magnitude 0.0.

As Mars sets at 4 am, **Jupiter** starts to put in an appearance, over in the southeast at magnitude –1.9 in the constellation of Libra.

Mercury is another dawn object, putting in its best morning show of the year. It rises in the morning twilight, to the lower left of Jupiter, at 6 am mid-month, with a magnitude of –0.4.

Neptune, in Capricornus, shines faintly at magnitude 7.9 and sets at about 8 pm.

Uranus (magnitude 5.9) currently lies in Aquarius, dropping below the horizon at around 10 pm.

MOON

Venus lies near the crescent Moon on 4 December, in the early evening sky. On 11 December, the Moon is near Mars, and on 13 December it passes just below the Pleiades, or Seven Sisters, at around 7.30 pm. The Moon, just past full, lies near Saturn on 18 and 19 December. In the early morning on 27 December, you'll find the crescent Moon near Jupiter.

WEST

WEST

EAST

December's Object Hyades Cluster
December's Picture
Radiant of Geminids

Mars
Satrn
Moon

MOON		
Date	**Time**	**Phase**
1	3.03 pm	New Moon
8	9.38 am	First Quarter
15	4.18 pm	Full Moon
23	7.39 pm	Last Quarter

◄ *The Double Cluster in Perseus, as photographed by Michael Stecker using a 200 mm telescope. The image took 20 minutes to capture, on ISO 400 print film.*

SPECIAL EVENTS

13 December: It is the maximum of the **Geminid** meteor shower, which lasts from 7 to 16 December. The meteors are debris shed from an asteroid called Phaethon, and are therefore quite substantial – and hence bright. This year, however, the Moon is full on 15 December, and its glare will interfere with the show.

21 December, 6.34 pm: Today is the Winter Solstice. As a result of the tilt of Earth's axis, the Sun reaches its lowest point in the heavens as seen from the northern hemisphere: we get the shortest days, and the longest nights.

DECEMBER'S OBJECT

The V-shaped **Hyades** star cluster, which forms the 'head' of Taurus, the bull, doesn't hold a candle to the dazzling Pleiades. But it's the nearest star cluster to the Earth, and it forms the first rung of the ladder in establishing the cosmic distance scale. By measuring the speeds of the stars in the cluster, astronomers can establish their properties, and use these results to find the distances to stars that are farther away.

In legend, the Hyades feature in many myths, often as female figures, for example the nymphs who cared for Bacchus as a baby. The interpretations we like most are those of the Romans, who called the stars 'little pigs', and the Chinese vision of them as a 'rabbit net'.

The Hyades cluster lies 151 light years away, and contains about 200 stars. The stars are all around 790 million years old, which is very young on the stellar scale, and they may have a celestial twin. It turns out that the Praesepe, the Beehive Cluster in Cancer, is the same age, and its stars are moving in the same direction. It may well be that the two clusters share a common birth.

Date	Rise (am)	Set (pm)
1	7.44	3.55
2	7.45	3.55
3	7.47	3.54
4	7.48	3.53
5	7.49	3.53
6	7.51	3.53
7	7.52	3.52
8	7.53	3.52
9	7.54	3.52
10	7.55	3.52
11	7.56	3.52
12	7.57	3.52
13	7.58	3.52
14	7.59	3.52
15	8.00	3.52
16	8.01	3.52
17	8.02	3.52
18	8.02	3.52
19	8.03	3.53
20	8.03	3.53
21	8.04	3.54
22	8.04	3.54
23	8.05	3.55
24	8.05	3.55
25	8.06	3.56
26	8.06	3.57
27	8.06	3.58
28	8.06	3.58
29	8.06	3.59
30	8.06	4.00
31	8.06	4.01

SUNRISE AND SUNSET

DECEMBER'S PICTURE

The **Double Cluster** is a beautiful pair of star clusters, and is also a glorious sight in binoculars. Medium-sized telescopes reveal that each cluster contains about 300 stars, although this is the tip of the iceberg: there are thousands of stars in residence. The stars are very young (in astronomical terms!), at between three and five million years old.

DECEMBER'S TOPIC
The Christmas Star

Brilliant Venus, high in the sky all this festive month, will focus attention on the nature of the Christmas Star. What was the object that drew the Magi out of the East, and directed them to Bethlehem, where Jesus lay in a manger? And why did King Herod – who felt threatened by the Christ-child becoming a future king himself – confess that he was not aware of the star?

The answers are subtle, and possibly unanswerable, being rooted in the mists of antiquity and hearsay. First of all, we need to establish the date of the birth of Christ. It was certainly not AD 1, but a date somewhat before that. A sixth-century cleric called Dionysius Exiguus tried to establish the dates of important events by logging in the lengths of the reigns of all the Roman emperors. Unfortunately, he missed one out, with the result that Jesus was born BC!

So what might have been in the sky to lure the Magi from the East? In 5 BC, there was a comet visible, according to the Chinese. Or it might have been a nova – a star that brightens dramatically. But neither theory explains why Herod could not see these celestial portents.

Possibly the key is the fact that the Magi were astrologers, and thus accomplished at calculating future events in the sky. In 7 BC, they worked out that the planets Jupiter and Saturn would draw together on three occasions to create a rare 'triple conjunction'. To astrologers, unlike astronomers, conjunctions are meaningful: they combine the characteristics of each planet. Jupiter was the king of the planets; Saturn was the planet of the Jews. The message was clear: the King of the Jews was to be born around the time of the middle of these conjunctions, which took place on 6 October that year.

So there was no brilliant star, and even the birth of Jesus might be a myth. But taking together all the astronomical evidence, David Hughes – a world expert on the Christmas Star – reckons that the best-guess date for Christ's birth is 15 September 7 BC. It's a good excuse for an early Christmas celebration!

There's always something to see in our Solar System, from planets to meteors or the Moon. These objects are very close to us – in astronomical terms – so their positions, shapes and sizes appear to change constantly. It is important to know when, where and how to look if you are to enjoy exploring Earth's neighbourhood. Here we give the best dates in 2005 for observing the planets and meteors (weather permitting!), and explain some of the concepts that will help you to get the most out of your observing.

THE INFERIOR PLANETS

A planet with an orbit that lies closer to the Sun than the orbit of Earth is known as *inferior*. Mercury and Venus are the inferior planets. They show a full range of phases (like the Moon) from the thinnest crescents to full, depending on their position in relation to the Earth and the Sun. The diagram shows the various positions of the inferior planets. They are invisible at *conjunction* and best viewed at their eastern or western *elongations*.

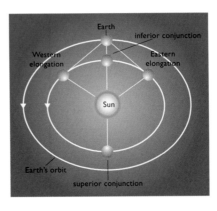

◄ At eastern or western elongation, an inferior planet is at its maximum angular distance from the Sun. Conjunction occurs at two stages in the planet's orbit. Under certain circumstances an inferior planet can transit across the Sun's disc at inferior conjunction.

Mercury is close to the Sun and is visible only for a period of roughly a week, six to eight times a year. From the northern hemisphere, it is best spotted around sunset in the spring during an eastern elongation from the Sun, and around dawn in the autumn during a western elongation. Sweep the approximate area of the sky with binoculars to locate the planet soon after sunset.

○ In mid-March 2005, Mercury is at its greatest elongation (east) of the Sun and is visible during dusk after sunset. In late June and early July, it is again visible in the early evening. In December, it is at its greatest elongation (west) and is visible in the dawn before sunrise.

● Maximum elongations of Mercury in 2005		
Date	Time (UT)	Separation
12 Mar	18:19	18° 20' 24" east
26 Apr	16:23	27° 09' 43" west
9 July	03:18	26° 15' 23" east
23 Aug	23:20	18° 24' 13" west
3 Nov	15:50	23° 30' 52" east
12 Dec	12:43	21° 04' 41" west

Venus lies farther from the Sun than Mercury. Its phases can be seen in good binoculars or a small telescope, while a larger telescope is needed to see features in the upper atmosphere. Venus is at its brightest about 36 days either side of inferior conjunction.

● In January 2005, Venus is visible just before dawn. From May until the end of the year, it is a prominent evening object, reaching greatest elongation (east) in November.

● Maximum elongation of Venus in 2005		
Date	Time (UT)	Separation
Nov 3	19:32	47° 06' 10" east

▶ *Superior planets are invisible at conjunction. At quadrature the planet is at right angles to the Sun as viewed from Earth. Opposition is the best time to observe a superior planet.*

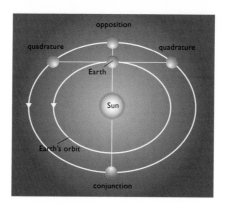

THE SUPERIOR PLANETS

The superior planets are those with orbits that lie beyond that of the Earth. They are Mars, Jupiter, Saturn, Uranus, Neptune and Pluto. The best time to observe a superior planet is when the Earth lies between it and the Sun. At this point in the planet's orbit, it is said to be at *opposition*.

● Progress of Mars through the constellations	
Early Jan–early Feb	Scorpius
Mid Feb–mid March	Sagittarius
Late March–early May	Capricornus
Mid May–early June	Aquarius
Mid June–late July	Pisces
Early Aug–early Sep	Aries
Mid Sep–late Oct	Taurus
Early Nov–end of year	Aries

Mars is a disappointing sight through a small telescope. Larger amateur telescopes, however, reveal the dark markings on the surface, changes in the polar ice caps, as well as Mars' phases and the progress of dust storms. Because Mars rotates in approximately 24 hours and 37 minutes, the features change during the night.

● *Mars reaches opposition on 7 November 2005 and is best placed for observation towards the end of the year. Its progress through the constellations is shown in the table at left.*

Magnitudes

Astronomers measure the brightness of stars, planets and other celestial objects using a scale of *magnitudes*. Somewhat confusingly, fainter objects have higher magnitudes, while brighter objects have lower magnitudes; the most brilliant stars have negative magnitudes! Naked-eye stars range from magnitude −1.5 for the brightest star, Sirius, to +6.5 for the faintest stars you can see on a really dark night. As a guide, here are the magnitudes of selected objects:

Sun	−26.7
Full Moon	−12.5
Venus (at its brightest)	−4.6
Sirius	−1.5
Betelgeuse	+0.4
Polaris (Pole Star)	+2.0
Faintest star visible to the naked eye	+6.5
Pluto	+14
Faintest star visible to the Hubble Space Telescope	+31

Jupiter is a very rewarding target. Even a small telescope will reveal some of the bands in its atmosphere and the Great Red Spot. Larger instruments will reveal many of the smaller features in the clouds, such as white spots. The 10-hour rotation period of Jupiter's upper atmosphere makes it an ideal candidate for short-exposure CCD or video imaging. Drawing Jupiter can be challenging because of the rapid rotation.

The four largest satellites of Jupiter – Callisto, Europa, Ganymede and Io – can be seen in most binoculars. Their orbits can be plotted using even moderate-sized telescopes and their transits and occultations can be observed.

● *Jupiter lies in the constellation of Virgo through most of 2005, moving into Libra in December. It is best placed for observation in the first half of the year, particularly around the time it reaches opposition on 3 April.*

Saturn is perhaps best known for its ring system, which can be seen in small telescopes. Larger telescopes will reveal the structure of the main rings, the banding of the planet's atmosphere and changes such as the appearance of white spots.

The angle at which the rings are seen changes over a 30-year period. Recording this cycle makes an interesting long-term project. Some of Saturn's brightest satellites – Dione, Iapetus, Rhea, Titan and Enceladus – are visible in larger telescopes. Like the Galilean satellites of Jupiter, their orbits can be plotted and their transits observed.

● *Saturn starts 2005 in the constellation of Gemini and moves into Cancer on 16 July. It is at opposition on 13 January and is well placed for observation in late winter and early spring.*

Uranus is just visible with the naked eye, and is better seen with good binoculars or a small telescope. With a powerful telescope, it appears as a small blue-green disc. The brighter satellites can be picked up in CCD images.

● *Throughout 2005 Uranus lies in the constellation of Aquarius, though for much of the early part of the year it is drowned out in the glare from the Sun. Visibility improves during the summer, and it reaches opposition on 1 September.*

Neptune is visible in good binoculars or a small telescope, and is a pale blue-green. Its largest satellite, Triton, may be seen in large amateur instruments.

● *Neptune spends 2005 in the constellation of Capricornus. It is not visible early in the year, and is best viewed in the summer. By July, Neptune is above the horizon all night, and it reaches opposition on 8 August.*

Pluto is very faint, magnitude 14, and difficult to locate even in the largest amateur instruments.

SOLAR AND LUNAR ECLIPSES

Solar eclipses, particularly total solar eclipses, are among the most exciting sky sights you can see. A solar eclipse occurs when the Moon's shadow falls on Earth.

For a solar eclipse to occur, the Moon must be perfectly in line between the Sun and Earth. This happens at least twice a year, and sometimes as many as five times. However, you do have to be in the right location on Earth to see the eclipse.

● *There are two solar eclipses in 2005, on 8 April and 3 October. The former will be seen from the south Pacific and parts of South America. The latter will be visible from Madrid through northern and eastern Africa and out into the Indian Ocean; it will appear as a partial eclipse from the UK.*

A **lunar eclipse** occurs when the Moon passes through Earth's shadow. As with solar eclipses, it may be total or partial, depending on whether the Moon passes completely or partially through the dark central part of Earth's shadow.

● *There is a lunar eclipse on 17 October 2005. It will be visible in North America and Asia, though unfortunately not in northern Europe.*

Astronomical distances

For objects in the Solar System, like the planets, we can give their distances from the Earth in kilometres. But the distances are just too huge once we reach out to the stars. Even the nearest star (Proxima Centauri) lies 25 million million km away. So astronomers use a larger unit, the *light year*. This is the distance that light travels in one year, and it equals 9.46 million million km.

Here are the distances to some familiar astronomical objects, in light years:

Proxima Centauri	4.2
Betelgeuse	427
Centre of the Milky Way	24,000
Andromeda Galaxy	2.9 million
Most distant galaxies seen by the Hubble Space Telescope	13 billion

---

Angular separations

Astronomers measure the distance between objects, as we see them in the sky, by the angle between the objects, in degrees (symbol °). From the horizon to the point above your head is 90 degrees. All around the horizon is 360 degrees.

You can use your hand, held at arm's length, as a rough guide to angular distances, as follows:

Width of index finger	1°
Width of clenched hand	10°
Thumb to little finger on outspread hand	20°

For smaller distances, astronomers divide the degree into 60 arcminutes (symbol '), and the arcminute into 60 arcseconds (symbol ").

▶ *Where the dark central part (the umbra) of the Moon's shadow reaches the Earth, a total eclipse is seen. People located within the penumbra see a partial eclipse. If the umbral shadow does not reach Earth (right), an annular eclipse is seen. This type of eclipse occurs when the Moon is at a distant point in its orbit and is not quite large enough to cover the whole of the Sun's disc.*

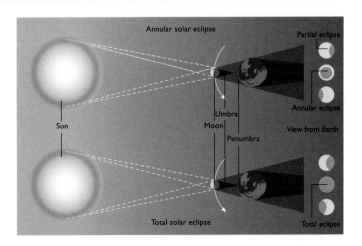

Dates of maximum for selected meteor showers	
Meteor shower	date of maximum
Quadrantids	3 January
Lyrids	22 April
Eta Aquarids	5 May
Perseids	12/13 August
Orionids	21 October
Leonids	17 November
Geminids	13 December

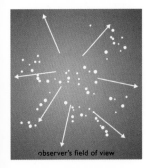

▲ *Meteors from a common source, occurring during a shower, enter the atmosphere along parallel trajectories. As a result of perspective, however, they appear to diverge from a single point in the sky.*

METEOR SHOWERS

Shooting stars – or *meteors* – are tiny particles of interplanetary dust, known as *meteoroids*, burning up in the Earth's atmosphere. At certain times of year, the Earth passes through a stream of these meteoroids (usually debris left behind by a comet) and a *meteor shower* is seen. The point in the sky from which the meteors appear to emanate is known as the *radiant*. Most showers are known by the constellation in which the radiant is situated.

When watching meteors for a coordinated meteor programme, observers generally note the time, seeing conditions, cloud cover, their own location, the time and brightness of each meteor and whether it was from the main meteor stream or not. It's also worth noting any details of persistent afterglows (trains) and fireballs, and making counts of how many meteors appear in a given period.

COMETS

Comets are small bodies in orbit about the Sun. Consisting of frozen gases and dust, they are often known as 'dirty snowballs'. When their orbits bring them close to the Sun the ices evaporate and dramatic tails of gas and dust can sometimes be seen.

A number of comets move round the Sun in fairly small, elliptical orbits in periods of a few years; others have much longer periods. Most really brilliant comets have orbital periods of several thousands or even millions of years. The exception is Comet Halley, a bright comet with a period of about 76 years. It was last seen in 1986.

Binoculars and wide-field telescopes provide the best views of comet tails. Larger telescopes with a high magnification are necessary to observe fine detail in the gaseous head (coma). Most comets are discovered with professional instruments, but a few are still found by experienced amateur astronomers.

Deep sky objects are 'fuzzy patches' that lie outside the Solar System. They include star clusters, nebulae and galaxies. To observe the majority of deep sky objects you will need binoculars or a telescope, but there are also some beautiful naked eye objects, notably the Pleiades and the Orion Nebula.

The faintest object that an instrument can see is its *limiting magnitude*. The table gives a rough guide, for good seeing conditions, for a variety of small- to medium-sized telescopes.

We have provided a selection of recommended deep sky targets, together with their magnitudes. Some are described in more detail in our 'Object of the month' features. Look on the appropriate month's map to find which constellations are on view, and then choose your objects using the list below. We have provided celestial coordinates, for readers with detailed star maps. The suggested times of year for viewing are when the constellation is highest in the sky in the late evening.

Limiting magnitude for small to medium telescopes	
aperture	limiting magnitude
50	+11.2
60	+11.6
70	+11.9
80	+12.2
100	+12.7
125	+13.2
150	+13.6

RECOMMENDED DEEP SKY OBJECTS

Andromeda – autumn and early winter

M31 (NGC 224) Andromeda Galaxy	3rd magnitude spiral galaxy, RA 00h 42.7m Dec +41° 16'
M32 (NGC 221)	8th magnitude elliptical galaxy, a companion to M31. RA 00h 42.7m Dec +40° 52'
M110 (NGC 205)	8th magnitude elliptical galaxy RA 00h 40.4m Dec +41° 41'
NGC 7662 Blue Snowball	8th magnitude planetary nebula RA 23h 25.9m Dec +42° 33'

Aquarius – late autumn and early winter

M2 (NGC 7089)	6th magnitude globular cluster RA 21h 33.5m Dec –00° 49'
M72 (NGC 6981)	9th magnitude globular cluster RA 20h 53.5m Dec –12° 32'
NGC 7293 Helix Nebula	7th magnitude planetary nebula RA 22h 29.6m Dec –20° 48'
NGC 7009 Saturn Nebula	8th magnitude planetary nebula; RA 21h 04.2m Dec –11° 22'

Aries – early winter

NGC 772	10th magnitude spiral galaxy RA 01h 59.3m Dec +19° 01'

Auriga – winter

M36 (NGC 1960)	6th magnitude open cluster RA 05h 36.1m Dec +34° 08'
M37 (NGC 2099)	6th magnitude open cluster RA 05h 52.4m Dec +32° 33'
M38 (NGC 1912)	6th magnitude open cluster RA 05h 28.7m Dec +35° 50'

Cancer – late winter to early spring

M44 (NGC 2632) Praesepe or Beehive	3rd magnitude open cluster RA 08h 40.1m Dec +19° 59'
M67 (NGC 2682)	7th magnitude open cluster RA 08h 50.4m Dec +11° 49'

Canes Venatici – visible all year

M3 (NGC 5272)	6th magnitude globular cluster RA 13h 42.2m Dec +28° 23'
M51 (NGC 5194/5) Whirlpool Galaxy	8th magnitude spiral galaxy RA 13h 29.9m Dec +47° 12'
M63 (NGC 5055)	9th magnitude spiral galaxy RA 13h 15.8m Dec +42° 02'
M94 (NGC 4736)	8th magnitude spiral galaxy RA 12h 50.9m Dec +41° 07'
M106 (NGC4258)	8th magnitude spiral galaxy RA 12h 19.0m Dec +47° 18'

Canis Major – late winter

M41 (NGC 2287)	4th magnitude open cluster RA 06h 47.0m Dec –20° 44'

Capricornus – late summer and early autumn

M30 (NGC 7099)	7th magnitude globular cluster RA 21h 40.4m Dec –23° 11'

Cassiopeia – visible all year

M52 (NGC 7654)	6th magnitude open cluster RA 23h 24.2m Dec +61° 35'
M103 (NGC 581)	7th magnitude open cluster RA 01h 33.2m Dec +60° 42'
NGC 225	7th magnitude open cluster RA 00h 43.4m Dec +61 47'
NGC 457	6th magnitude open cluster RA 01h 19.1m Dec +58° 20'
NGC 663	Good binocular open cluster RA 01h 46.0m Dec +61° 15'

Cepheus – visible all year

Delta Cephei	Variable star, varying between 3.5 and 4.4 with a period of 5.37 days. It has a magnitude 6.3 companion and they make an attractive pair for small telescopes or binoculars.

Cetus – late autumn

Mira (omicron Ceti)	Irregular variable star with a period of roughly 330 days and a range between 2.0 and 10.1.
M77 (NGC 1068)	9th magnitude spiral galaxy RA 02h 42.7m Dec –00° 01'

Coma Berenices – spring

M53 (NGC 5024)	8th magnitude globular cluster RA 13h 12.9m Dec +18° 10'
M64 (NGC 4286) Black Eye Galaxy	8th magnitude spiral galaxy with a prominent dust lane that is visible in larger telescopes. RA 12h 56.7m Dec +21° 41'
M85 (NGC 4382)	9th magnitude elliptical galaxy RA 12h 25.4m Dec +18° 11'
M88 (NGC 4501)	10th magnitude spiral galaxy RA 12h 32.0m Dec.+14° 25'
M91 (NGC 4548)	10th magnitude spiral galaxy RA 12h 35.4m Dec +14° 30'
M98 (NGC 4192)	10th magnitude spiral galaxy RA 12h 13.8m Dec +14° 54'
M99 (NGC 4254)	10th magnitude spiral galaxy RA 12h 18.8m Dec +14° 25'
M100 (NGC 4321)	9th magnitude spiral galaxy RA 12h 22.9m Dec +15° 49'
NGC 4565	10th magnitude spiral galaxy RA 12h 36.3m Dec +25° 59'

Cygnus – late summer and autumn

Cygnus Rift	Dark cloud just south of Deneb that appears to split the Milky Way in two.
NGC 7000 North America Nebula	A bright nebula against the background of the Milky Way, visible with binoculars under dark skies. RA 20h 58.8m Dec +44° 20'
NGC 6992 Veil Nebula (part)	Supernova remnant, visible with binoculars under dark skies. RA 20h 56.8m Dec +31 28'
M29 (NGC 6913)	7th magnitude open cluster RA 20h 23.9m Dec +36° 32'
M39 (NGC 7092)	Large 5th magnitude open cluster RA 21h 32.2m Dec +48° 26'
NGC 6826 Blinking Planetary	9th magnitude planetary nebula RA 19 44.8m Dec +50° 31'

Delphinus – late summer

NGC 6934	9th magnitude globular cluster RA 20h 34.2m Dec +07° 24'

Draco – midsummer

NGC 6543	9th magnitude planetary nebula RA 17h 58.6m Dec +66° 38'

Gemini – winter

M35 (NGC 2168)	5th magnitude open cluster RA 06h 08.9m Dec +24° 20'
NGC 2392 Eskimo Nebula	8–10th magnitude planetary nebula RA 07h 29.2m Dec +20° 55'

Hercules – early summer

M13 (NGC 6205)	6th magnitude globular cluster RA 16h 41.7m Dec +36° 28'
M92 (NGC 6341)	6th magnitude globular cluster RA 17h 17.1m Dec +43° 08'
NGC 6210	9th magnitude planetary nebula RA 16h 44.5m Dec +23 49'

Hydra – early spring

M48 (NGC 2548)	6th magnitude open cluster RA 08h 13.8m Dec –05° 48'
M68 (NGC 4590)	8th magnitude globular cluster RA 12h 39.5m Dec –26° 45'

M83 (NGC 5236)	8th magnitude spiral galaxy RA 13h 37.0m Dec –29° 52'
NGC 3242 Ghost of Jupiter	9th magnitude planetary nebula RA 10h 24.8m Dec –18°38'

Leo – spring

M65 (NGC 3623)	9th magnitude spiral galaxy RA 11h 18.9m Dec +13° 05'
M66 (NGC 3627)	9th magnitude spiral galaxy RA 11h 20.2m Dec +12° 59'
M95 (NGC 3351)	10th magnitude spiral galaxy RA 10h 44.0m Dec +11° 42'
M96 (NGC 3368)	9th magnitude spiral galaxy RA 10h 46.8m Dec +11° 49'
M105 (NGC 3379)	9th magnitude elliptical galaxy RA 10h 47.8m Dec +12° 35'

Lepus – winter

M79 (NGC 1904)	8th magnitude globular cluster RA 05h 24.5m Dec –24° 33'

Lyra – spring

M56 (NGC 6779)	8th magnitude globular cluster RA 19h 16.6m Dec +30° 11'
M57 (NGC 6720) Ring Nebula	9th magnitude planetary nebula RA 18h 53.6m Dec +33° 02'

Monoceros – winter

M50 (NGC 2323)	6th magnitude open cluster RA 07h 03.2m Dec –08° 20'
NGC 2244	Open cluster surrounded by the faint Rosette Nebula, NGC 2237. Visible in binoculars. RA 06h 32.4m Dec +04° 52'

Ophiuchus – summer

M9 (NGC 6333)	8th magnitude globular cluster RA 17h 19.2m Dec –18° 31'
M10 (NGC 6254)	7th magnitude globular cluster RA 16h 57.1m Dec –04° 06'
M12 (NCG 6218)	7th magnitude globular cluster RA 16h 47.2m Dec –01° 57'
M14 (NGC 6402)	8th magnitude globular cluster RA 17h 37.6m Dec –03° 15'
M19 (NGC 6273)	7th magnitude globular cluster RA 17h 02.6m Dec –26° 16'
M62 (NGC 6266)	7th magnitude globular cluster RA 17h 01.2m Dec –30° 07'
M107 (NGC 6171)	8th magnitude globular cluster RA 16h 32.5m Dec –13° 03'

Orion – winter

M42 (NGC 1976) Orion Nebula	4th magnitude nebula RA 05h 35.4m Dec –05° 27'
M43 (NGC 1982)	5th magnitude nebula RA 05h 35.6m Dec –05° 16'
M78 (NGC 2068)	8th magnitude nebula RA 05h 46.7m Dec +00° 03'

Pegasus – autumn

M15 (NGC 7078)	6th magnitude globular cluster RA 21h 30.0m Dec +12° 10'

Perseus – autumn to winter

M34 (NGC 1039)	5th magnitude open cluster RA 02h 42.0m Dec +42° 47'
M76 (NGC 650/1) Little Dumbbell	11th magnitude planetary nebula RA 01h 42.4m Dec +51° 34'

NGC 869/884 Double Cluster	Pair of open star clusters RA 02h 19.0m Dec +57° 09' RA 02h 22.4m Dec +57° 07'

Pisces – autumn

M74 (NGC 628)	9th magnitude spiral galaxy RA 01h 36.7m Dec +15° 47'

Puppis – late winter

M46 (NGC 2437)	6th magnitude open cluster RA 07h 41.8m Dec –14° 49'
M47 (NGC 2422)	4th magnitude open cluster RA 07h 36.6m Dec –14° 30'
M93 (NGC 2447)	6th magnitude open cluster RA 07h 44.6m Dec –23° 52'

Sagitta – late summer

M71 (NGC 6838)	8th magnitude globular cluster RA 19h 53.8m Dec +18° 47'

Sagittarius – summer

M8 (NGC 6523) Lagoon Nebula	6th magnitude nebula RA 18h 03.8m Dec –24° 23'
M17 (NGC 6618) Omega Nebula	6th magnitude nebula RA 18h 20.8m Dec –16° 11'
M18 (NGC 6613)	7th magnitude open cluster RA 18h 19.9m Dec –17 08'
M20 (NGC 6514) Trifid Nebula	9th magnitude nebula RA 18h 02.3m Dec –23° 02'
M21 (NGC 6531)	6th magnitude open cluster RA 18h 04.6m Dec –22° 30'
M22 (NGC 6656)	5th magnitude globular cluster RA 18h 36.4m Dec –23° 54'
M23 (NGC 6494)	5th magnitude open cluster RA 17h 56.8m Dec –19° 01'
M24 (NGC 6603)	5th magnitude open cluster RA 18h 16.9m Dec –18° 29'
M25 (IC 4725)	5th magnitude open cluster RA 18h 31.6m Dec –19° 15'
M28 (NGC 6626)	7th magnitude globular cluster RA 18h 24.5m Dec –24° 52'
M54 (NGC 6715)	8th magnitude globular cluster RA 18h 55.1m Dec –30° 29'
M55 (NGC 6809)	7th magnitude globular cluster RA 19h 40.0m Dec –30° 58'
M69 (NGC 6637)	8th magnitude globular cluster RA 18h 31.4m Dec –32° 21'
M70 (NGC 6681)	8th magnitude globular cluster RA 18h 43.2m Dec –32° 18'
M75 (NGC 6864)	9th magnitude globular cluster RA 20h 06.1m Dec –21° 55'

Scorpius (northern part) – midsummer

M4 (NGC 6121)	6th magnitude globular cluster RA 16h 23.6m Dec –26° 32'
M7 (NGC 6475)	3rd magnitude open cluster RA 17h 53.9m Dec –34° 49'
M80 (NGC 6093)	7th magnitude globular cluster RA 16h 17.0m Dec –22° 59'

Scutum – mid- to late summer

M11 (NGC 6705) Wild Duck Cluster	6th magnitude open cluster RA 18h 51.1m Dec –06° 16'

M26 (NGC 6694)	8th magnitude open cluster RA 18h 45.2m Dec –09° 24'

Serpens – summer

M5 (NGC 5904)	6th magnitude globular cluster RA 15h 18.6m Dec +02° 05'
M16 (NGC 6611)	6th magnitude open cluster, surrounded by the Eagle Nebula. RA 18h 18.8m Dec –13° 47'

Taurus – winter

M1 (NGC 1952) Crab Nebula	8th magnitude supernova remnant RA 05h 34.5m Dec +22° 00'
M45 Pleiades	1st magnitude open cluster, an excellent binocular object. RA 03h 47.0m Dec +24° 07'

Triangulum – autumn

M33 (NGC 598)	6th magnitude spiral galaxy RA 01h 33.9m Dec +30° 39'

Ursa Major – all year

M81 (NGC 3031)	7th magnitude spiral galaxy RA 09h 55.6m Dec +69° 04'
M82 (NGC 3034)	8th magnitude starburst galaxy RA 09h 55.8m Dec +69° 41'
M97 (NGC 3587) Owl Nebula	12th magnitude planetary nebula RA 11h 14.8m Dec +55° 01'
M101 (NGC 5457)	8th magnitude spiral galaxy RA 14h 03.2m Dec +54° 21'
M108 (NGC 3556)	10th magnitude spiral galaxy RA 11h 11.5m Dec +55° 40'
M109 (NGC 3992)	10th magnitude spiral galaxy RA 11h 57.6m Dec +53° 23'

Virgo – spring

M49 (NGC 4472)	8th magnitude elliptical galaxy RA 12h 29.8m Dec +08° 00'
M58 (NGC 4579)	10th magnitude spiral galaxy RA 12h 37.7m Dec +11° 49'
M59 (NGC 4621)	10th magnitude elliptical galaxy RA 12h 42.0m Dec +11° 39'
M60 (NGC 4649)	9th magnitude elliptical galaxy RA 12h 43.7m Dec +11° 33'
M61 (NGC 4303)	10 magnitude spiral galaxy RA 12h 21.9m Dec +04° 28'
M84 (NGC 4374)	9th magnitude elliptical galaxy RA 12h 25.1m Dec +12° 53'
M86 (NGC 4406)	9th magnitude elliptical galaxy RA 12h 26.2m Dec +12° 57'
M87 (NGC 4486)	9th magnitude elliptical galaxy RA 12h 30.8m Dec +12° 24'
M89 (NGC 4552)	10th magnitude elliptical galaxy RA 12h 35.7m Dec +12° 33'
M90 (NGC 4569)	9th magnitude spiral galaxy RA 12h 36.8m Dec +13° 10'
M104 (NGC 4594) Sombrero Galaxy	Almost edge on 8th magnitude spiral galaxy. RA 12h 40.0m Dec –11° 37'

Vulpecula – late summer and autumn

M27 (NGC 6853) Dumbbell Nebula	8th magnitude planetary nebula RA 19h 59.6m Dec +22° 43'

EQUIPMENT GUIDE – WHAT'S NEW?

Today more than ever before the choice of telescopes and equipment is bewildering. About 25 years ago, say, the choice was pretty simple – either a refractor, with a lens, which gave sharp images but was expensive in the larger sizes – or a reflector, with a mirror, which was cheaper in large sizes but required more maintenance. An advanced amateur astronomer might have a sturdily mounted 200 mm reflector in the back garden, maybe in a shed with a removable roof.

Then along came catadioptric telescopes, which combined mirrors and lenses to give a compact tube, making larger instruments more portable. They featured many innovations, including clever mountings with motor drives, which had previously been thought of as a bit of a luxury. But it didn't stop there. In the 1990s, the US manufacturers Meade and Celestron realized they could design a hand-held computer with a database of the whole sky that would run the telescope from scratch. Just set the telescope up, tell it where it is, the time and date, give it a couple of bright stars to get its bearings from, and it will then take you to any other object in the sky. This is known, unsurprisingly, as a GO TO mount. The great thing about GO TO mounts is that, unlike the the more traditional equatorial mountings, they do not need to be carefully aligned on the Earth's polar axis for ordinary visual observing.

▼ *The Explorer 130M telescope is a popular starter instrument for the price of a reasonable digital camera*

Developments in the East

For a while, it looked as if Meade and Celestron had everything sewn up, with a full range of instruments and highly developed GO TO mounts. But then along came the Chinese firm of Synta. In the past, many Far Eastern telescopes have been of uncertain quality. Apart from top-level Japanese manufacturers such as Vixen, there were numerous manufacturers in Hong Kong and Taiwan who mostly produced small refractors that promised everything but delivered nothing. Synta, however, has made a name for itself by producing beginners' instruments of good quality, and is believed to make many of the small telescopes in the Celestron range. UK importers Optical Vision say that their best seller is the Explorer 130M – a basic 130 mm (5-inch) reflector on an equatorial mount, equipped with sensible magnifications of 36 to 180 and, notably, a motor drive.

From the same stable comes the Startravel-150, a 150 mm (6-inch) short-focus refractor. At one time a 6-inch refractor was regarded as an advanced observatory instrument, but Synta has brought it within reach of many amateurs. Like other standard refractors it suffers from a certain amount of false colour, usually blue fringes around bright objects. Many observers counter this by using one of the Baader filters, such as the Contrast Booster or the Fringe Killer, which selectively filter out the blue wavelengths to give crisper images with refractors in particular. These filters screw into a standard 31.7 mm eyepiece, and they are available in the UK from David Hinds Ltd.

Picture perfect

A revolution has swept astro-imaging. Photography of the Moon and planets has always been the poor relation of visual observing, with Earth's turbulent atmosphere making it hard to capture details on the planets. While the eye can snatch even the briefest steady moment to see fine detail, you have to be extremely lucky to catch the same moment on film or even a CCD. However, people have found that they can use cheap webcams – essentially low-quality video cameras for computer users – to make video sequences of the view through the telescope, although they are only sensitive enough to record the brighter objects, basically those within the Solar System. The real breakthrough has come with the development of software that can run through thousands of frames, captured at rates of around 25 a second, to select only the sharpest ones. The software then combines the frames into a single image and allows the user to apply computer processing techniques to sharpen them up even more.

▼ The lunar crater Clavius, photographed by Damian Peach through an 80 mm refractor using a Philips ToUcam webcam.

The results are truly amazing. Webcams costing no more than a cheap holiday camera can produce images of the Sun, Moon and planets that surpass any taken previously using large professional telescopes. One need hardly bother to go to a high-altitude site any more. Modest telescopes in ordinary suburban gardens can produce spectacular results. You still need to take great care in focusing and telescope alignment, but the results can be truly stunning, and few people bother to use film to image the planets these days.

The Philips ToUcam is by far the most popular webcam for astro-imaging, but Meade is now supplying its own webcam, known as the Lunar and Planetary Imager (LPI), as standard equipment with every large telescope sold.

Telescope mounts

In addition to improved telescope designs, there are now many more ways in which you can mount the telescope. Astronomers have always known that no matter how good your telescope, it is pretty useless if the mounting is poor. The fork mounts that the early catadioptrics used – and indeed generally still use – are well suited to their task, but they have limited stability and accessibility to the whole sky. The first GO TO mounts were of this type. Many experienced observers preferred the more traditional German mount, which requires a counterweight but allows more flexibility and is more sturdy.

Within the past year, Japanese manufacturer Vixen has introduced a new design of German equatorial mount. Back in the 1980s Vixen changed people's way of thinking about telescope mounts with their Super Polaris mount, which included precision motors and an optional built-in polar axis telescope. For the first time you could take your telescope to a dark-sky site, quickly align the mounting with the Earth's axis, and rely on the motors to drive the telescope precisely with the minimum of correction; it was a boon to deep-sky astrophotographers.

Vixen's latest Sphinx mount is a major redesign. Previously, the motors were bolt-on options, but now they are integrated within the housing, so reducing the weight requirements for the counterbalance (always a bugbear of the German mount). They have also produced a radical new GO TO handset: it actually shows the night sky on its display, allowing a much more friendly interface than that of former designs.

Observe the Sun

Another area of astronomy that has recently been opened up is solar imaging using narrowband filters. At one time, anyone who wanted to view the spectacular prominences at the edge of the Sun had to construct an elaborate imaging

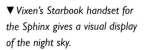

▼ Vixen's Starbook handset for the Sphinx gives a visual display of the night sky.

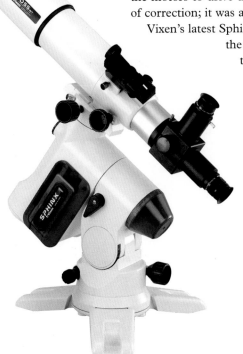

◄ The Vixen Sphinx mount in its table-top variant, carrying an 80 mm short-focus refractor.

▶ *A digital camera snap of the view through a Personal Solar Telescope (PST) by Swiss amateur Gregory Giuliani and colleagues.*

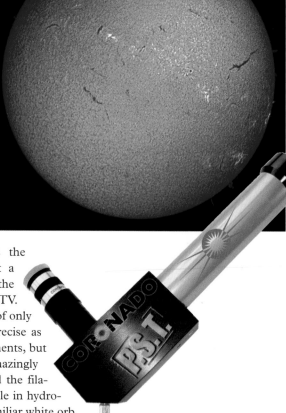

system. Then along came filters that showed just the light from hydrogen atoms on the Sun as emitted by these prominences, but these 'hydrogen-alpha filters' were regarded as for specialist use only. In recent years, companies such as Coronado and Solarscope have produced filters and dedicated telescopes of high quality, but at prices that would normally buy you a fully featured large GO TO telescope or even a cheap car.

Now, however, Coronado has introduced what they refer to as the Personal Solar Telescope (PST) at a fraction of the original price – about the same as that of a 28-inch widescreen TV. The telescope itself has an aperture of only 40 mm and the filters are not as precise as those on the more expensive instruments, but enthusiastic users say that it gives amazingly sharp views of the prominences and the filaments on the Sun that are only visible in hydrogen-alpha light. It transforms the familiar white orb into a mass of intricate detail, and has given amateur astronomers a new source of enjoyment – and one that you don't have to lose sleep over!

▲ *The Coronado PST allows you to view solar prominences without waiting for an eclipse.*

ACKNOWLEDGEMENTS
All star maps by Wil Tirion/Philip's, with extra annotation by Philip's.
Artworks © Philip's.
All photographs from Galaxy.
64t G. Giuliani/P. Confino/P. Chavalley
16, 49, 62 Damian Peach
45 Philip Perkins
12, 24, 28, 32 Robin Scagell
8, 36, 40, 52 Michael Stecker
61 Optical Vision
63 Orion Optics
21 Dave Tyler
64b Telescope House

WEBSITES FOR UK SUPPLIERS
Synta (Optical Vision):
www.opticalvision.co.uk
Meade and Coronado (Telescope House):
www.telescopehouse.co.uk
Celestron and Baader (David Hinds):
www.dhinds.co.uk
Vixen (Orion Optics):
www.orionoptics.co.uk
Solarscope Ltd:
www.sciencecenter.net/solarscope/